LEONIS

LEONIS

or

The Lion's Brood

by
Horace Bell

Edited by
Gerry Keesey Hoppe

*From an unpublished manuscript written by Horace Bell in the Early 1900s
— the original can be found in the Huntington Library, San Marino, California.
Note: Chapters IV, V and VI appeared in the Los Angeles* Graphic *on April
10, 17 and 24, 1909.*

ACKNOWLEDGEMENTS

The Leonis Adobe Association is most grateful to Mrs. Hoppe for finding this manuscript, for her research and her editing Bell's rather preliminary manuscript. We are grateful to the Huntington Library for permission to use the manuscript, and to Mr. James A. Phillips, III, great grandson of Major Horace Bell for permission to publish it.

We hope that you the reader, will enjoy this book. Some of you may be able to assist the Leonis Adobe Assn. with additional information about the occurrences mentioned herein, or the history and early residents of the Leonis Adobe. We would most appreciate hearing from you. Simply write to us at 23537 Calabasas Road, Calabasas, California, 91302, and if you haven't seen the Leonis Adobe, do come and pay us a visit.

— Ray Phillips,
President,
Leonis Adobe Assn.

FOREWORD

Several years ago I set out to learn all I could about a 19th-century Southern California rancher named Miguel Leonis. What information I had gathered from library sources and museum lore was just enough to intrigue, but not enough to satisfy. Practically all of what has been printed about Leonis is derived directly from Horace Bell's depiction of him in *On the Old West Coast.* According to Bell, "Leonis the Basque, King of Calabasas, . . . was a giant in stature and strength, a perfect savage in nature, besotted in ignorance, so illiterate that he could not read a word in any language."

One of the ironies of life is that within a few generations of one's death, if you are remembered at all it is only because of what someone else wrote about you. And woe be to the person who incurs a negative opinion from a contemporary the likes of Horace Bell. This prominent Los Angeles attorney was also editor of his own journal, *The Porcupine,* which routinely editorialized against anything and anyone Bell deemed lacking in character or moral propriety. Even so, he seemed more intent on poking fun at Leonis than attacking his character. In a chapter titled "Spit in the Mouth of Hell," Bell has a 44-foot-long prehistoric monster emerge from the depths of Lake Elizabeth only to be chased by the Big Basque, who had "a well-known aversion to any rival in his domain."

During his lifetime, Miguel Leonis was respected as a rancher/businessman who was able to accomplish much in the 30-plus years that he lived in California. Considering that he did not read or write, Miguel did very well. The emigrant from France in the late 1850s went on to become a prosperous cattle and sheep rancher, reputedly one of the wealthiest men in Los Angeles county, when Los Angeles county covered most of Southern California.

Finding credible non-Horace Bell sources for information on Leonis proved very difficult. Miguel was a French Basque; he did not mix socially with Anglo-Americans, and certainly he did not speak English. Yet most of what has been written about Leonis has come from an Anglo press —or was based on the reminiscences of Anglo old-timers of the area, persons who clearly would have had a bias against the man who fought against their homesteading on ranch lands he perceived as his. Since Miguel did not read or write, we can assume he did not keep a journal to enlighten us on his thought processes. Who is there to give us an objective view of this man? So far, I have yet to find any such person— but here is the next best thing: another perspective on Leonis from Horace Bell himself. Knowing what Bell had previously written about the Big Basque, I was amazed and delighted to discover the existence of this unpublished manuscript, which he sub-titled *"The Lion's Brood,"* for here he paints a completely different picture.

There is a problem with this account in that it cannot be categorized as completely factual or total fiction. What Horace Bell set out to write was not Miguel's life story but a novel, with Miguel as its protagonist hero. Some parts are tales of rollicking adventure, while other passages have the clear ring of truth. Because I had done so much research on Leonis and the people in his life, I immediately recognized the characters in this story, even when Bell played games with their names— Stephanus Black for Stephen M. White, for instance. In the manuscript Bell used ficticious but rather indentifiable names for most of his characters, as with White. Likely the reason was to avoid lawsuits! However, when he invented a character for the story he used an obviously ficticious name, such as "Senor Muyoscuro." These names have been left intact. Basically, most of Bell's characters were real people. Bell captures their essence rather than absolute truth—his skill lies not in historical documentation but in masterful caricature.

In the story that follows, I have edited Bell's words for clarity and smoothness. I also added chapter endnotes whenever I was sure Bell had deviated from fact or when I could corroborate his account with credible alternative sources.&

— Gerry Keesey Hoppe
1991

ABOUT THE AUTHOR

The always controversial Maj. Horace Bell cut an imposing figure in Los Angeles. He practiced law in the city during the late 1880s and had the additional distinction of being editor of his own newspaper, *The Porcupine*. Bell's caustic and often inflammatory journal urged immediate reform from the governing powers of Los Angeles, city and county. Under its motto "Fearless, Faithful and Free," the journal lampooned and caricatured the many Anglo sharpers who invaded the southern region—many of whom dispossessed the hospitable Californios forever of their gracious 18th-century lifestyle. Upon the *Porcupine's* first issue, the *Los Angeles Times* commented: "True to its nature each quill was on end and deuced sharp. Somebody will be looking for the editor with a shotgun if he doesn't smooth them down a bit."

The Scottish/Irish native of Indiana was 22 and an avid adventure seeker when he first came to Los Angeles in 1852. At the time, the census of the pueblo showed a population of only 1,610, yet in 1850 the unruly little settlement had reportedly averaged a homicide a day—in an era when record keeping customarily acknowledged the deaths only of white men. Bell joined the California Rangers to search out elusive desperadoes such as Joaquin Murrieta. In 1856 he left for Nicaragua as a soldier of fortune with William Walker's army. He went to Mexico in 1859, where he joined the army of Benito Juarez. When the American Civil War broke out, Bell hurried to his home state to join the 6th Indiana regiment and later served as a scout for the Union Army.

After the Civil War, Bell returned to Los Angeles with his young wife and two small children. This was in July, 1866. The little family followed the Butterfield Southern Overland Stage Route and stopped at

Horace Bell as he appeared in later years; about the time he wrote this book.

Willow Grove (now known as El Monte), a few miles east of their destination. As far as they could see were the bleached bones of thousands of cattle, dead of thirst from the drought of the previous two years. In Los Angeles, the brown plains surrounding the nondescript pueblo were devoid of trees except for a few near the church on the plaza. The town's water came from an open public ditch, called the zanja, from which each subscribing family's barrels were filled twice a week.

Bell purchased 35 acres of farmland south of the pueblo, near what is now Pico and Figueroa streets. On this site he built a wooden cottage and settled down to a farmer's life. Several years later, at his wife Georgia's urging, Bell decided to enter the legal profession. He brought home the necessary books to study and eventually appeared before the Supreme Court in Los Angeles, where he passed an oral examination—the sole requirement to become a practicing lawyer in those days. From its beginning in 1872, Bell's legal career spanned some 25 years.

It was in Bell's capacity as an attorney that he knew Miguel Leonis, the French Basque who controlled the west end of the San Fernando Valley. Leonis was a wealthy rancher, involved in numerous court cases in which Bell often represented the opposing side. The powerful, physically impressive Big Basque apparently caught the imagination of the young adventurer/attorney, now tethered by the needs of his rapidly expanding family. Horace Bell and his wife Georgia eventually had a total of 11 children.

In 1899 Georgia Bell died. In 1903 Bell moved to Berkeley and at 78 married Mrs. Emily Jane Culver. He began writing stories; not too successfully, as only one was published during his lifetime. Among the unpublished works was the manuscript of this book. The book's editor, Mrs. Gerry K. Hoppe, first found two chapters of it which were published in the Los Angeles paper called *The Graphic* in 1909. Later she visited the Huntington Library, asked for material on Miguel Leonis, and was told they had nothing. Upon asking for materials regarding Horace Bell she was handed several boxes, one of which contained the typed manuscript of this book, missing the two chapters published in *The Graphic!* She, and we, sent the missing chapters to the Huntington, so now their manuscript is reasonably complete.

Through Horace Bell's telling of the story that follows we learn the ins and outs of sheep-raising, the disgraceful machinations of the city's legal fraternity during the 1880's, and Bell's own version of how Miguel Leonis died—he never did accept that the death was caused by an accident.

We believe the part of the story referring to Leonis as working to finance a Basque revolution to be a story line invented by Bell to enable him to tell what he knew of Leonis in a more interesting manner. But who knows? Certainly the Basques are still at it. A recent newspaper story tells of five Basque political bombings in one week!

Over a period of time an amazing amount of Bells story has turned out to be true, and verifiable by independent sources. With the exception of "Father Jean, head of the monastery," "El Senor Muyoscuro" loosely translated as "a very obscure man" (and a good "name" for a secret agent!) and several other similar, obviously invented names, all of Bell's major characters are identifiable persons. Even "John Peter," whom you will meet in the first scene at the monastery, was a resident in a Basque monastery, and was ejected for the reason given. In later life he was jailed, in Los Angeles, for forging Leonis' name, just as Bell describes. Later on, when Bell describes the activities of some of his fellow lawyers, and what an unscrupulous, pettifogging group they were, he speaks from personal knowledge. Not all were so. Stephen M. White who, with Bell, finally won a widow's settlement for Espiritu Leonis, went on to become a United States senator. His bronze statue stands in the Los Angeles harbor area.

Certainly no other person was as well qualified to write about Leonis as was Bell. Not only were they co-residents of a small city (Leonis had a 17 acre ranch in what is now east Los Angeles, that he used as a town house. Its location was just south of the Harbor Freeway as it turns into the Santa Ana Freeway), but Bell was on the opposing (and usually winning) side of several lawsuits involving Leonis; finally ending up on Leonis' side, and winning a case for him. In these cases, and the long struggle of Espiritu to be declared Leonis' legal wife, he heard testimony by Leonis, Espiritu, Leonis' relatives, his friends and his enemies. Bell had a talent for good storytelling, which involved the use of exaggeration. The only out-and-out exaggeration I can find in this story is Bell's calling the Leonis Adobe Espiritu's "castle". Even those of us who have worked for the last 25 and more years to preserve the Leonis Adobe and love the place cannot bring ourselves to call it a "castle", but we are more than willing to forgive Horace Bell for calling it so!☙

— Gerry Keesey Hoppe,
with additions by
Ray Phillips, President,
Leonis Adobe Assn.

CONTENTS

I

The Fugitive at the Monastery

Our story begins in the French Basque village of Cambo during the year 1855 and ends in Southern California, in the region known as the Cahuenga, in 1889:[1]

In the province of France known as Basses Pyrenees, there exists a great old monastery. Located near the village of Cambo, this mass of irregular piles of buildings has stone walls so weathered, door fastenings so rusty and a tile roof so patched and faded, it looks at once timeless and of great antiquity. Clouded in the mysteries of its misty past, the venerable old monastery provides no outward clue as to its origin, age or purpose—its doors and lower windows securely locked to shield it from curious eyes. Even a cursory glance, however, hints that here is something with a history reaching centuries before the coming of Christ. The order of monks fortressed inside bear little resemblance to priests of modern times. These claim an independent brotherhood—the aim and primary object of which is to afford succor for the distressed and asylum for the fleeing fugitive.

One wintry night near Christmas, 1855, the head of this institution sat at a table in the large reception hall as he pored over an ancient manuscript. A porter entered the room.

"Yes?" Father Jean asked.

"Reverend Sir, a fugitive stands at the outer gate and demands shelter."

"Bring him in without delay so we can see who he is—and why and from whom he flies."

Minutes later, the porter ushered in a young man of most striking appearance. He was clad in the garb of the mountaineers of the Basque provinces—and armed to the teeth. Girded to his waist were a pair of Colt revolvers and a long straight, two-edged knife. The young man stood a full six feet four inches in height, as erect as an American Indian. He appeared to weigh at least two hundred pounds. As he stood still and dignified in the presence of the monk, muscles quivering in suppressed excitement, his piercing eyes flashed as burning balls of fire.

Blood stains were discernible on his garments, and Father Jean noted that his hands were clenched and his teeth seemed ground together in suppressed rage. He appeared to be no more than twenty-one or twenty-two years of age.

"Ha! Miguelon, it is you—and again!—what is it this time?" queried the monk as he gazed in admiration at the splendid piece of living statuary standing before him.

"Yes, Father, it is I. Now, however, I am more than just Miguelon. You see before you Miguel, 'rey de los contrabandistas.'"

"King of the smugglers, eh? When were you made king and who crowned you, my great lion cub?"

"The Spanish customs officers with whom I have so recently fought —and who went back to the King's customs house less in numbers than when they left in search of Miguel Leonis. Look here, Father." The young giant produced a placard printed in Spanish. It offered the equivalent of one hundred dollars reward for the arrest and delivery to Spanish customs authorities of one 'Miguel, King of the Smugglers' and fifty dollars for any member of his band of outlaws.[2]

"I think they have honored you beyond your just deserts. There is little merit to being a smuggler—and even less to being designated the leader of such outlaws. Especially for someone such as you, Miguel, one of the Lion's Brood — a prince by blood and birth, a natural leader, if only we Basques had our rights and you your natural inheritance." Miguel could hardly suppress his amusement. "If I am a smuggler king

Miguel Leonis (c. 1879)
1824-1889

and a princely leader of the Basques by right of inheritance—may I ask why it is you do not invite such a king to a seat? And why is that flagon of wine there so temptingly exposed, when I am famished from thirst?!"

"Why certainly, Miguelon! Of course! Sit down, sit down. Fill the mug and fill it again. Slake your thirst."

Going to the door, the monk called down the hallway for assistance: "Ho! Jean Pierre!" Shortly, a sullen boy came down the hall. "Jean Pierre, quickly!" Father Jean said. "We need some food for our guest—bread, cheese, cold meat, olives—but first bring water and clean towels. See how the fellow bleeds! Bring linen for bandages."

"Now, my brave fellow," he turned to Miguel. "Tell me, why all this blood?"

"It's only a prick on the shoulder from a bayonet. You know, Father, for a short time I was hemmed in by those rascals, and I had a hard tussle getting out. This is my only scratch."

Water, towels, lint bandages and clean clothing made such a change for the comfort and betterment of the gigantic youth that, when he sat down to his repast in a quiet restful manner, he appeared far different from when he had first entered. He ate ravenously.

"We were carrying some Lyons silks across the border when we ran into the Spanish Customs guards. With two men, I engaged the guards in a fight so the rest of our band could escape with the goods. In a sense, Spain gained nothing and we lost nothing—Delfin and Pierre got away without a scratch and are safe."

"You are safe also," Father Jean said, "for as long as you remain here. But you will be hunted and hounded as soon as you leave these walls."

Miguel nodded. "But I have to go away from here. Surely I will not turn monk and join your order. Yet I know leaving here means war. Ah, if I could raise these provinces against Spain—and against France also —I know we could defy them!"

"My brave Leonis, we will see about that. I need some time to think, ponder, study, advise with you—I have so much to tell! Things so strange, so grand, so sublime—and yet unknown to the world—absolutely unknown to all!—save those monks who have gone before and of whom I am the successor. I hold the key to a great historical mystery, and

I will lay it before you, Miguel, because you are entitled to know all! You will dare all, win all. You can redeem us from two thousand years of subjugation by contemptible peoples!"

"Now Miguel," the monk continued, "first you need some rest. And I have some work upon which I was engaged when you arrived." He rang a small bell and the boy Jean Pierre appeared in the doorway.

"Conduct this young man to his room and see that he is well cared for. Tomorrow morning he will breakfast with me."

Saying his thanks, the youthful Hercules followed the sullen-faced urchin into the corridor. Father Jean was left alone with his thoughts in the great reception hall.❧

Endnotes:

1. The full name of the French village is Cambo-les-bains, birthplace of Miguel Leonis. The Basque province in which it is located was formerly called Basses-Pyrenees, renamed in 1970 to Pyrenees-Atlantiques. In Southern California, the term Cahuenga is an old Indian name identifying the general Hollywood region.

2. According to William A. Douglass and Jon Bilbao in *Amerikanuak: Basquea in the New World,* the Basque people on both sides of the Spanish/French border regard the division established in 1512 as somewhat artificial: "Few regard as 'illegal' the two-directional clandestine smuggling of goods and persons across the border." This is even more understandable when one considers the physical geography of the Basque region. Measuring from either north to south or east to west, it is barely a hundred miles across. (pp 12-13)

    For generations the Basques have been fighting both France and Spain for independence. They fought the two "Carlist Wars" against Spain in the 19th century, being finally defeated in 1876. This did not stop the Basque separatist movement. As of 1992 assassinations of French and Spanish officials and bombing of public buildings continue.

2

Miguel and Father Jean Make Plans

The next morning Father Jean awaited Miguel in his private dining room. It had thick walls, deep windows and a lofty ceiling. Laden on the table were all manner of things; capon, coffee, chocolate, wine, brandy and other appetising fare. Miguelon—which means Big Miguel—entered the room ushered by the cunning, leering rascal Jean Pierre.

"Good morning Don Miguel!" the father superior greeted him. "Let us speak in our native Basque language rather than French, and use Spanish only if we cannot avoid it.[1] I call you Don because Spain has raised you from a lowly condition to one of royalty. Now you are a Spanish Don. So, Don Miguel, did you sleep well? I hope you have a good appetite. May I offer you a little eau de vie? Ah, mal rayo! Here I am the very first thing using the French language."

Miguel knew enough of any language to understand the invitation. He helped himself to a glass of brandy from an old earthenware flagon that graced the board.

Breakfast is a slow business except to Americans, and to those with a hard day's work before them. In a monastery it is a particularly long drawn-out and most formal proceeding. Father Jean and Miguel sat for hours, the monk doing the talking and the fugitive listening intently.

"It is a long, long story, my boy, and to recount it all in detail would require days, nights, weeks, even months! Suffice it to say that you, as your surname indicates, are one of the 'Lion's Brood.' I see you do not understand the meaning of the expression. Let me recount to you a brief

"Tauletchea", Cambo, Basses Pyrenees, France. Ancestral home of the Leonis family, and birthplace of Miguel Leonis. Watercolor from photographs taken by Mr. and Mrs. Leonis Malburg in 1965. A typical Basque stone with redtile roof farmhouse, still standing in good repair, and occupied by two families. The surrounding farm has been subdivided recently. In earlier days the building combined house and barn; the two large doors at the extreme right led into the barn.

history of our people dating back two thousand years. Only then will you understand. You have doubtless heard of the long continued state of war—covering a period of more than two hundred years—between ancient Carthage and Rome? It ended finally in the demolition and erasure from the earth's surface of imperial Carthage. The people of Carthage were utterly exterminated thereby, except for a small few who scattered to the four winds. Some sought refuge here—in this very place! Think of it, Miguel. Our people, the Basques of Spain and France, originated as a Carthaginian colony!"[2]

Miguel shook his head affirmatively. "If you say so. But I still do not understand what you mean by the 'Lion's Brood.'"

"It means this. When war was raging on land and sea between Carthage and Rome, the Carthaginian leader Hamilcar[3] invaded Spain, which Rome claimed was part of the Roman empire. Hamilcar did not invade Spain to make war on its people, the Iberians, but to enlist them for aid in his operations against Rome. Hamilcar founded this colony as a resting place. His plan for the invasion was to first enter France, then cross the Alps and descend upon the plains of Italy to attack Rome from the rear. After a long and bloody contest in Spain and in these mountains, Hamilcar was forced to return to Carthage. To his sons, he handed down a heritage of eternal hatred and war against Rome, a heritage to be bequeathed to all future generations until Rome is destroyed. He designated these heirs—his sons—as the Lion's Brood."

"So, you see, Miguel Leonis," Father Jean continued, "you who have lived here all your life unsuspecting—your family name signifies the present-day Lion's Brood, and such you are. Think of it! This presumed monastery remains as the only monument left standing to commemorate the greatest people ever to shake the earth with their mighty acts of war and accomplishments in peace. Hamilcar himself constructed this building! Here we guard the history of his lost race— lost except for the Basque mountaineers, who know nothing of its history or the truth of their descent. The secrets of history are enclosed within these walls, Miguel—to be given to the world only when our people shall have achieved their independence, set up their own government, destroyed Rome and restored Carthage. Now all this can come to pass, for the genealogical tree of Hamilcar has been preserved, root and branch. We have it here! You, my son, are a lineal descendant of that great Carthaginian chief through the line of Hamilcar's son, Hannibal."

"There is more," the monk continued triumphantly. "Hannibal died in this building. His ashes repose here and we guard his tomb. After the destruction of Carthage, Hannibal took refuge with Antiochus the Great, and as a treaty condition, Rome demanded the surrender of the fugitive. It has been said that Hannibal took poison and died rather than fall into the hands of his hated enemies. But it is not true. When

Hannibal crossed from Syria into Spain, he found a haven in this monastery. Here he lived in peace and here he died. And now here are you, his descendant—as am I, guardian of his sacred precincts."

Beaming, Father Jean paused to see the effect of his words on the young Basque. He leaned forward. "Here is the best part: Through the centuries Carthaginian oracles prophesied and proclaimed that someone such as you, whom the Spanish have designated a smuggler king, will be the one to regenerate the Carthaginian race. Stand up, my boy, and let me look at you! Yes! You are a king from your head to your foot. You are every inch a king and no longer a mere smuggler."

Miguel Leonis smiled slowly and shook his head. "I am a strange sort of king. The king of the smugglers dares not set his foot outside the door of this refuge. If I am indeed a descendant of Hannibal, what good is that to me?! My main options now are to get out of the country completely or be caught and shot—either by the Spaniards, who dominate us from across the line, or by the French, who dominate us on both sides of the border. That nothing but an imaginary line should divide our people in two! French Basques, Spanish Basques, what does it matter? We are all Basques!" Miguel began to warm to his subject. "And you tell me, Father, that we are in effect Carthaginians? Well, I am not much versed in history, but I once heard the story of the destruction of Carthage—about the wars between the Carthaginians and the Romans, and the founding of Cartagena in Spain. New Carthage was founded by the Carthaginians during their peninsular operations against Rome, was it not? I know of these things, have heard of them somewhat. Not in great detail, though, because I do not have much opportunity to read. Herding sheep in the mountains, protecting them from wild animals and such like hard service—and perhaps a certain amount of early schooling in contraband transactions—has been my hard lot in life. So, I am not much of a scholar.[4] As I said, what good is it to me to be a descendant of a mighty man like Hannibal and be deemed his successor, when I am here, cooped up like a rat in a trap? Let me ask you this. What if Spain should make a demand on France and the French send their police here to your door, demanding my surrender. If that should happen, Father, what would you do?"

"What would I do? Should French minions even attempt to pass the portals of this refuge, I would hurl the curse of Rome upon them. They would not dare to enter. The poor fools—little would a curse from Rome hurt anyone, but still they believe in it and fear it. We who falsely assume its power can yet intimidate them with such talk."

"What exactly does the curse of Rome mean—sending people to hell?"

"Exactly. Only I doubt it has any such potency."

"But you are a Roman priest," Miguel said in mocking tones. "How can you talk so!"

"I am Roman in name only. At heart I am a Carthaginian. The fact is, I accept as an entailment—as do all monks in this monastery—an eternal antipathy toward Rome. We may not live to see it, but the day will come when the Carthaginians will destroy Rome and Carthage will be rebuilt. We are the Carthaginians, Miguel, and here will be our Carthage."

"I do not know that I share your vision, Father, but I do believe the Basques are a wonderful people who deserve better than what they have. They are men of great strength, and the women are as brave as the men. We number hundreds of thousands. I suspect we are capable of raising a mighty army of Basques that Spain and France would be powerless to put down. Our mountain fastnesses are our best defense and safeguard."

"Certainly, my son, we could raise an army of men. And the women by their labor would support the men at war. There is one major thing lacking, however—and that is money. Waging war requires substantial resources. To equip an army we must have money, for it is essential we have a military chest. We would need to control a seaport—Bilbao, for instance, or Bayonne. Unfortunately, even in this poor monastery, our treasury is very small. How sad that the Basque people are so poor—impoverished in everything except industry and the courage to persevere! But if we had five million francs, Miguel—then we could purchase arms, munitions and military supplies. We could boldly proclaim our independence, and maintain it for all time against all of Europe![5]"

Miguel looked doubtful. "Five million francs? I cannot even imagine such a large amount."

"Think of a million as a thousand thousands," the monk answered. "You can rest assured that I have studied this matter well. Others who have gone before me studied the situation also—and it is all plain enough. For the Basque people, revolution has always been feasible except for the money."

The two men sat in silence for a few minutes while Miguel considered what the father superior had told him. "Very well, perhaps I can do something," he said. "Help me go away to some foreign land, Father, and I will work to acquire the riches we need for our cause. Send me to California, the great land of gold. With my strength, perseverance, industry—somehow—I will accumulate the necessary money for you. I promise, I will either send or deliver it to you personally."

"A good plan," answered Father Jean. "The best of our people have left this infertile land for foreign countries, where they became rich and distinguished. But they never return to their homeland! They prefer to enjoy their newly acquired riches and honors in their adopted lands. Many have gone to Africa, still others to South America, Mexico, and in recent years California. If you go to California, Miguel, very likely you will, I am sure, acquire great wealth, but you will also want to remain there to enjoy it. You will not return to assist your impoverished countrymen in their effort to recover what is rightfully theirs—a government for themselves."

"You are mistaken in this, Father. You have awakened in me a mighty impulse. You have raised my thoughts above the low level of a smuggler's ambitions and put aspirations in my heart that will expire only with my life. I will go to California. I will bring five million francs to this very monastery, which I will place in your hands, or in those of your successor, for the purposes of a great Basque war. Our independence will be established! Our cry shall be 'Eternal hatred toward Rome.' You will see. We will destroy Rome and rebuild Carthage. By this I mean we will start the mighty ball rolling— and if we do not reach our goal ourselves, those who come behind us will. It is settled then. I must go to California! But how to get out of here and safely onboard a ship? The problem racks my brain. Father, let me leave that to your wisdom. Just help me to escape from this country. Get me to California."

"Very well, my brave boy, I will see that you reach California— and may God speed you! I will devise a plan to get you out of here and safely on shipboard, with coin sufficient to pay your way to the land of gold."

The conference ended. Having long since passed its meridian, the sun ceased casting its penetrating rays through the grated windows of the dining hall. Miguel departed from the room. Father Jean retired to the great library to engage himself in serious meditation.

All monks are presumed to be old. Not so with Father Jean. He was a relatively young man of not more than thirty-five years—a man of most remarkable appearance, with a solid muscular figure, dark complexion, piercing black eyes, and a massive head indicative of a high order of intelligence. Altogether, his countenance was pleasing and benevolent.

In the massive library filled with thousands of quaint old volumes, the monk remained seated for a long time in silence and deep concentration. Then he started to pace. "Yes, I make no mistake. This young giant Miguel Leonis is the redeemer of our race, the man foretold by the oracles. Since I first heard of his encounter with the customs guards, I have had my eye upon him. Such a wonderful production of nature, this young man is—a hero from the ground up. He has great ambition, courage, strength, industry, perseverance and he is truthful, an honest man. I believe in him."

He reached the end of the room and turned to pace back. "Miguel will go to California. I can arrange it. First I must get him on shipboard—a difficult task now that word is out about the customs incident. The man is safe only within these sheltering walls—outside, every rock on the roadside will have eyes for him. The very leaves on the trees will whisper when he passes, for those bent on his capture must already swarm the countryside. But I can get him out and on a ship! I will make my plans and carry them out immediately!"&

Endnotes

1. A primary indicator of the uniqueness of the Basque culture is its language, which has no conclusive links to that of any other group of people. The Basques' primal identity is in being "Euskaldunak"—literally "speakers of Euskera," the term for the Basque language.

2. The Basques are known as the mystery people of Europe, for no one knows with certainty their true origin. According to Douglass and Bilbao in their book *Amerikanuak: Basques in the New World,* present-day Basque territory in the western Pyrenees has had continuous human occupation since the Middle Paleolithic or for at least the last 70,000 years (p. 10). In the story recounted by Father Jean, author Horace Bell expresses his own personal theory of the Basques' origin.

3. Hamilcar Barca was the father of Hannibal (247-183 B.C.), the Carthaginian general who was to cross the Alps with elephants during the outset of the Second Punic War. Hamilcar took Hannibal as a child to Spain and made him swear eternal enmity toward Rome, an oath Hannibal evidently never forgot.

4. Miguel Leonis was no scholar. According to California court records, he was illiterate in any language.

5. Basques in Europe have had a history of rebellion that continues to this day. During the two Carlist wars of the 19th century, Basques pitted themselves against Spaniards in a struggle for greater political autonomy and freedom of cultural expression. The modern Basque separation movement was started by Sabino Arana y Goiri.

Leonis

3

Escape to Marseilles — Arrival in California

everal plans were devised by Father Jean to enable Miguel to leave the monastery for a seaport and board a ship departing from Spain or France. After much discussion, one scheme after another was abandoned. Finally, the father superior presented Miguel with this proposition:

"If you could be conducted safely a few miles in the direction of Marseilles, do you suppose you could make your way through the mountains to that seaport? Although you would be constantly in French territory, this plan has the advantage that the risk of arrest is less so many miles from here, much less than were you to head for the nearest coast. Always bear in mind, my son, that you have a great purpose to accomplish. You must not take undue risk by either killing others or losing your own life—this is not as it was when you were in the contraband trade. I know a man, a merchant in Marseilles, who has a brother in California. If you are agreeable, I will give you a letter of introduction to this merchant and perhaps he will recommend you to his brother."

Miguel Leonis indicated his interest in the plan and Father Jean went on. "There must be nothing rash about this venture, Miguel," he said sternly. "You must slip unnoticed into Marseilles—this may be difficult because your great stature and muscular proportions attract attention to you. Yet it is very important that you not be seen! Now listen. I can direct you so you will find the residence of my friend with little trouble. You will be given his street and number, both of his mercantile house and of his private residence. The man's name is Pierre Mascarel and

17

he has dealt with us in matters of trade for years; he will be pleased to do us a service. Promise me you will faithfully carry out all instructions I give you, Miguel. Remember to act slowly, carefully, surely; do whatever is necessary to ensure your own safety. Once you reach the house of merchant Mascarel, the worst danger will be over."

Miguel readily acceded to the plan, pronouncing it good and expressing his confidence in the success of it. He promised to be very careful, more for Father Jean's sake than for his own, and assured the monk he would always bear in mind the great objective he was seeking to accomplish. The plan was settled.

A preliminary tactic was to send out the urchin Jean Pierre as a scout, so he could ascertain what was being done by the authorities and what plans had been laid for Miguel's capture. After a day or two of observation, Jean Pierre reported that the coast appeared clear. Father Jean's original idea had been to conceal Miguel in a wagon used for carrying produce from the country to the monastery, but Miguel objected strongly. The first thing the police would do is search all wagons, he said. He proposed instead to await a dark and stormy night, when he would go boldly forth and take his chances. Once the plan was finally settled, everything was prepared for Miguel's departure when the propitious time should arrive. New clothing was made. His revolvers were put in perfect order, to be carried under a cloak unseen. A sum of money was furnished him, together with a letter of credit to Mascarel and written instructions asking Mascarel's best services in the procuring of a passage out of Marseilles.

Within a few days, a great rain and windstorm came up and that night the moon was dark. Rather than leave from one of the gates of the monastery, Miguel Leonis—like Paul of Tarsus when he escaped from Damascus—let himself down from a window in a dark angle of the building, and quickly struck out for the mountains.

Nothing unusual occurred as he left the region or when he finally reached the coastal city of Marseilles. After nightfall, Miguel slipped into a wine house in the suburbs of that city. Seating himself in a remote corner, he ordered refreshments and conversed genially with the proprietor until, in the course of the evening, he idly inquired about the merchant Mascarel. The proprietor informed him that he knew the good man well, even where his residence was located. With additional directions from the wine house proprietor, Miguel was able to find Pierre Mascarel's house—and found him to be at home. Mascarel received the stranger hospitably and, after reading Father Jean's letter, assured Miguel of his intention to help him. Miguel was gratified that the merchant refrained from asking any questions as to why it was necessary for him to leave the country in such a secretive manner.

According to local advertisements, a sailing vessel was scheduled to depart for New York on the following day. Merchant Mascarel had shipped wines and other merchandise on this vessel, so he offered to procure passage for Miguel and get him onboard prior to her departure. All of this was safely accomplished and, in due time, the fugitive from Cambo arrived in New York. He managed to find his way to the West Coast, to the city of San Francisco in the golden state of California, where he felt himself a new man—a free man—safe and sound at last in the country from which he intended to someday carry away a million dollars.

What should be his first order of business? Miguel could not speak English, yet in San Francisco he found many who spoke French or Spanish. In the course of a day or two, he encountered some of his fellow Basques. His next step was to seek employment.

Wandering through the streets of the city, Miguel noticed a great wagon heavily laden with carcasses of slaughtered cattle, as it supplied many markets of the great city. Half a dozen men were expending their utmost strength to remove a beef carcass from the wagon and hang it on shambles in the market. Miguel watched with amusement until finally the last and largest of these carcasses was to be removed. Straightening to his full height, he asked permission to remove it. The men stared at him in silence but to a man they stepped back, standing ready to act as reinforcement in case he should fail. Lifting the massive carcass in his arms,

Miguel carried it into the market and hung it up with ease. At once he was a hero. The butchers and the beef handlers, who were Germans, spoke to him at once but could not make themselves understood. They gestured to him to ride with them to the slaughter house, where he was offered employment—an offer he immediately accepted. Soon Miguel was being paid double wages, since he alone could do the work of half a dozen men.

Among Miguel's possessions was a letter of introduction given him by the merchant Pierre Mascarel. It was to be delivered to Mascarel's brother Josef in Los Angeles. After Miguel had worked a year in his employ at the slaughterhouse, he left San Francisco with his pockets full of money he had saved and, arriving in Los Angeles, he at once presented himself to Josef Mascarel. Josef was a very rich, influential and hospitable man, and he received the gigantic stranger as a brother. And brothers they might well have been, for this Josef Mascarel was also very large—six feet four inches in height, weighing 250 pounds and then in the physical prime of his manhood. [1]

Sixteen months had elapsed since Miguel left the monastery at Cambo. For fourteen of those months, he worked at the slaughterhouses of San Francisco, earning a hundred dollars a month. Of the $500 Father Jean had furnished him for his voyage, upon Miguel's arrival in San Francisco he spent $200 of it. Miguel had worked his passage on the sailing vessel across the Atlantic, paid $150 steerage passage from New York to San Francisco and spent $50 for general expenses. With the $300 left from Father Jean in addition to his $1400 earned in wages, Miguel was able to present himself to Josef Mascarel in Los Angeles with a total of $1700 in his pocket. Whatever his outlay in San Francisco, it came from money he had earned in extra work. ◡◠

Endnotes

1. According to the Southern California Historical Society's *Los Angeles Pioneer Register* for the year 1899, Josef Mascarel was one of the first French settlers in this city. A native of France, he was born in Marseilles in 1816, served in the French navy and became a merchant ship captain. He settled in Los Angeles in 1845, when California was still under Mexican rule, and remained for more than 50 years. In later years he served both as mayor and as councilman, and he was much respected for his sound business sense. Mascarel is described as being "physically of stalwart proportions," standing more than six feet in height and weighing more than 200 pounds. (pp. 282-285) When he died in October 1899, the *Los Angeles Times* printed a death notice stating that he had accumulated a fortune conservatively estimated at half a million dollars (Oct. 7, 1899, p. 13) Horace Bell had a lifelong respect for Mascarel, whom he described in his book On The Old West Coast as "shrewd, vigilant and honest." (p.252)

Leonis

4

Miguel Comes to Los Angeles—Jose Mascarel

It was about the first of May, 1857, when our gigantic hero arrived in Los Angeles, and the country was in the full bloom and beauty of its primeval grandeur and loveliness. The ranchos were teeming with horses and cattle, and the sheep grazing industry had just opened up on the country, the Basques from the Pyrenees being the pioneers in sheep raising in Southern California.

Jose Mascarel was then a Los Angeles merchant, as merchants went in those pioneer days, who transacted business at his "Tendajon de la Campana." The store was designated by a long sign placed on the cornice of the adobe building—then quite new and pretentious—situated on the northeast corner of Upper Main and Marchessault streets.[1] "Tendajon de la Campana" means "great bell store," it being close to the parochial church that had been constructed on the west side of the city plaza in the year 1812.[2]

Jose Mascarel's tendajon was a remarkable place. It was one long room, at least forty feet in length by about eighteen in width, with a counter running from one end to the other, about four feet removed from the rear wall. In the center of the front section was the door, the only entrance, flanked by two small grated windows—iron grating through which an evil-disposed person could not even thrust an arm. Immediately opposite the door the counter was divided by a passageway. Behind that was a door cut through the rear wall that led to Mascarel's sleeping quarters—a portion of which constituted the kitchen and another part

Josef Mascarel, known in Spanish-speaking Los Angeles as Jose Mascarel.

the dining room. That is to say, Mascarel's kitchen, his dining room, and the bedroom were all the same room, which was as long as the store. At one end was the bedroom, at the other the kitchen, and in the middle was the dining area. All three were furnished primitively.

In the kitchen area, three round cobblestones supported a pot, wherein the day's beans were boiled and the meats stewed. Three other cobblestones were used for the purpose of heating a griddle wherein the female cook baked her tortillas. Opposite the tortilla bakery was a metate (stone grinder). This was a three-legged stone of Indian origin and Indian handicraft. About the size of an ordinary washboard, the device had one short leg in front and two high legs at each corner of the rear part of the stone, causing it to be set at an angle of about thirty degrees. A granite grinder, probably ten inches or a foot in length—about the size of the ordinary old-fashioned rolling pin—constituted the appendage of the metate.

Mascarel's woman cook would first boil a pot of corn in a solution of lye, which caused the peel of the corn to loosen. Then she would take the corn and put it in a tub of clean water and rub, rub, rub it with her hands until all of the husk came off, leaving the kernel clean, white and bare. Then the corn was ready for the metate, and the cook would bare her arms, lay aside her fly whisk and down on her knees she would go and start the mill to grinding. She would spread the corn out on the face of the metate, which was sort of ridged round with a border of granite, and she would rub the grain with her grinder until she had ground it fine. She piled up the grounded grain on a big, clean, flat board, until she had sufficient dough prepared for the bakery. Then the baking process would begin. How deftly she handled this corn dough, and how neatly she turned the tortillas; by the time she used up her beautiful pile of corn dough, she had a pile of tortillas half as high as herself if she were to lie prone on the ground.

While she was engaged in this industry, the beans would simmer and simmer and cook, and the carne (meat) would stew down— and all would be ready for Mascarel's breakfast. Mascarel breakfasted at about eleven o'clock. But the beans and the tortillas thus prepared would not all be consumed for breakfast. They would go into the tendajon and behind

A scene near the plaza, Los Angeles, probably taken in the late 1880's. Jose Mascarel's "Tendajon De La Campana" must have looked like the adobe in the foreground, after it got older.

the counter, forming part of the merchandise for sale. Beans and stewed beef were merchantable.

The two dishes did not constitute everything offered for sale in the tendajon's culinary department. On another cobblestone tripod the Indian cook brewed coffee, and, on still another, miscellaneous cooking chores were attended to. The place, that is, the whole room, was festooned with strings of chile peppers, jerked beef on strings, onions and garlic. Chile peppers were a staple article in Mascarel's Tendajon de la Campana, and they stood in greater importance than the strings of garlic. The Mexicans, principal patrons of the tendajon, were great consumers of chile peppers, while only the French people and the few Italians who were then in Los Angeles were purchasers and eaters of garlic.[3]

Piles of Mexican cheeses ornamented the principal shelf behind Mascarel's counter, and leaf tobacco constituted a staple article of commerce, tamales were displayed, being the fruits of the culinary handicraft of the feminine artist in the back room. Tamales were staples in those days, and if you wanted good tamales you had to go to the Tendajon de la Campana.

It was May when Miguel Leonis came to the tendajon, and the summer fruits had not yet ripened. Even so, watermelons were displayed for sale by the enterprising Mascarel. He had saved them over the winter to have the first ones on the spring market. Piles of corn husks neatly tied up in bundles were also a commodity to be purchased. And what for? Leaf tobacco and corn husks were two materials from which to form cigars, then called cigarritos. Another staple was panoche—ungrained sugar—moulded in a coffee cup—and at the time sold for two bits (25 cents) a cake.

Hundreds of bottles stood mustered in martial array on the second and third shelves of the tendajon. Some were marked as vin Bordeaux; others vino del pais, vino tinto, angelica, vino blanco, and aguardiente (whiskey). There were piles of gamuza, which means dressed and dyed deerskin, clothing made of dressed and dyed goat skins, beautifully embroidered, that is, pantaloons and jackets; also leggins. Mascarel offered some of everything, bridles, halters, spurs, riding boots, saddles, saddle blankets, serapes, ponchos from Peru, and beautiful hats made of vicuna, the amber-colored wool of an animal native to the Andes. Other important merchandise displayed at the tendajon included earthenware vessels from a griddle, upon which to bake tortillas, and a great water jar capable of holding thirty gallons of water, as well as all intermediate sizes. Metates also were for sale. In fact, such a store as Mascarel's probably has never been seen anywhere else. He had absolutely everything—everything that was old-fashioned and nothing new.

Mascarel had become rich from keeping that tendajon. In the rear he maintained a bakery, with pies, cakes and bread displayed on the shelves and counters. In a way, Jose Mascarel was a merchant prince—for he was a wise, sharp, sly fellow, this gigantic son of Gaul. He knew better how to make five dollars out of one dollar than any man who ever lived in Los Angeles. Jose Mascarel never got a dollar in his life that he was not able to convert to five dollars before he let it loose. And this is the man with whom Miguel Leonis dined on his first day in Los Angeles.

A jolly good time they had, too, because each took an immediate liking to the other.

Mascarel was then about forty years of age, and with the exception of his family help, the burly, muscular Indian woman who presided in the kitchen and did up things in the dormitory and waited on the table in the dining room, there was no other member of the Mascarel household.[4]

The business of the day over at the Tendajon de la Campana, the front door was closed and securely barricaded by placement of a scantling across and behind the door. This was propped by another scantling, or tranca, one end resting on the ground at the base of the counter and the other end securely against the piece across the door.

This was the manner of fastening all front doors in Los Angeles, which together with the iron-barred windows made the house impregnable from without. High walls guarded the rear, and in Los Angeles at that time the maxim was verified that "every man's house is his castle."

Seated at the pineboard table in the dining area with a burning tallow dip and a bottle of vino tinto between them, the magnific Mascarel began to chat socially with his guest.

"Surely, I am much obliged to my brother for sending me such a splendid-looking young man. What is your age?"

"Twenty-two years next September, sir."[5]

"How tall are you? I myself am six feet four—there's my mark on the door. Stand up." Miguel complied and stood with his back against the door. He just came even with Mascarel in height.

"Your weight?" was the next query.

"When I was weighed in San Francisco, I pulled down 220 pounds."

28

"I have the advantage of you there. I weigh 240 pounds—but my muscles are not hard like yours," feeling Miguel's arms and thighs. "Sacre Dieu, man, you must be made of twisted wire!"

The two sat down again.

"What do you propose to do here in California?" continued Mascarel.

"Herd sheep," came the response.

"Santa Maria, a man like you! Herding sheep! Any Indian can herd sheep as well as you can, and his master will get his services for $15 a month. What were you paid in the slaughterhouses of San Francisco?"

"One hundred dollars a month, with fifty cents for all extra hours."

"Pendejo!—and you came here to herd sheep?"

"Yes."

"At what wages?"

"The highest I can get."

"Have you any money?"

"Yes."

"How much?"

"Seventeen hundred dollars in gold. Here it is: I would like you to keep it for me."

"Oh, then you must mean you are going to buy sheep and herd them yourself."

"No, not at this time. Later, I will buy my own sheep and hire herders. I think it best to learn the country and its methods, so I am first going to hire myself out as a herder."

"You seem to be set on your own ideas," Mascarel remarked. "Very well, whatever you want. But what shall I do with your money?"

"What you see fit. When I need it, I will let you know—which I expect will be in about a year."

"All right, it will be here when you ask for it. But I still do not understand what possesses you to want to be a sheepherder."

"Well, good friend, I will tell you. I have been sixteen months in California and have considered my situation at length. The fact is, I know about sheep and sheep-raising methods in the Basque country, but I need to learn about this region—about the best manner of handling sheep here. It may be the two methods are quite different, and when I invest in this business I want to be assured of success. There are millions to be made here, and I intend to make one million dollars as soon as possible. I know I am going to make it, and I will make it out of sheep."

"Oh, ho! my best saint, you are an ambitious fellow, and I suppose you will aspire to the dignity of becoming 'Rey de Los Bosegueros' (king of the sheep herders)?"

"My aspirations are higher than that. Also, I want the benefit of your wisdom, your experience, your knowledge of the country, your friendship. If you can find me employment as a sheep herder for one year's duration, I will be satisfied."

"If that is all," said Mascarel, "it is done easily enough. Fifty miles from here is the rancho known as Tapo, in Santa Barbara county.[6] I happen to know that a friend of mine, who has a large herd of sheep, is looking for a foreman. Pierre Abadie is his name. He is in town now, and I am sure we will see him tomorrow." He rose from the table. "You had better get a good night's sleep. You have a long day ahead of you."

The next morning bright and early, the Tendajon de la Campana opened for business. Fires were lit under the culinary tripods, and soon coffee was served. Outside, it was a bright and beautiful day.

Mascarel and his guest were eating breakfast when who should drop in but the very man wanted, Pierre Abadie.

"Good morning, sir," said Mascarel, speaking in French, although so accustomed had he become to using Spanish he seldom spoke anything else. "When do you go to Tapo?"

"This very morning," Abadie replied. "My horse is tied at the door. I am on my way now."

Mascarel invited him to join them and Abadie accepted. As he seated himself at the table, Miguel was introduced and the subject of his employ discussed.

Miguel's answers to Abadie's questions being satisfactory— and his appearance so assuring—a bargain was made in a matter of minutes. Miguel was engaged as foreman at Tapo for one year at the rate of $60 a month plus his board.

"But how will you get there?" queried Abadie. "I only have the one horse."

"How far is it to the rancho?"

"To Tapo? Fifty miles," Abadie replied.

"What is fifty miles? I can walk. Just give me the directions and I will get there."

"Very well," said Abadie, impressed. "Cross the hills to Cahuenga, ten miles.[7] The people at that ranch will direct you twenty miles to the west; first to your right, which is San Fernando; next to your left, the Santa Susana pass; in-between is rancho El Escorpion. Should you go to either San Fernando or El Escorpion, you will be directed toward Tapo, which is over the mountains. I think, however, you had better go to El Escorpion. When you get there, tell the Indian Odon that I sent you. He will give you good cheer and send an Indian to guide you through the mountains to El Tapo. Well then, I shall expect you tomorrow evening." Whereupon Abadie mounted his horse and, with jingling spurs, galloped north on the calle principal—Upper Main street.

"Now, my young friend," observed Mascarel as they watched Abadie's retreating figure. "Before you leave for Tapo, I would like to offer you a little advice."

"It will be thankfully received," responded Miguel.

"You say you came here to make money. I also have the same object," said Mascarel. "My advice to you is simply this. Beware of these native Spanish women. You will do well to have nothing to do with them. If not, you will most assuredly be poor all your life. Do not be tempted to marry one, even if she may be rich in lands and in cattle. Such gastadoras (spendthrifts)!—these women beat all people on earth in their ability to reduce even a rich man to poverty. When you get a house of your own and find you need female help, get yourself an Indian woman like my Cerilda. They are great workers, and they come very cheap. Get an Indian woman, Miguel. When you no longer need her, you can sell or give her away."

"I may need a housekeeper at a future time," Miguel said, "but I am sure I do not want to marry in this country."

"Oh, you think there is no danger of your falling victim to the wiles of our beautiful senoritas?"

Miguel just smiled and made no answer. He slung his blankets over his shoulders and started to walk down the street.

"Adieu, Miguel, vaya con Dios," Mascarel called after him as he struck westward across the hills to Cahuenga.

It was nine o'clock in the morning when Miguel reached the large ranch house at Cahuenga. The ranch was situated at the fork of the road, the left side leading to Santa Barbara, the right to the Tulares by way of San Fernando.

A strange sight greeted him as he approached the great wide corridor of the long, low, red-tile-roofed building. Tied to a hitching post in front was a white man, his back laid bare and bleeding. Some rugged-looking vaqueros (cowboys) stood by, each armed with a stout willow switch. Seated on a magnificent, richly caparisoned horse was a gaudily dressed, dashingly handsome caballero, who quietly smoked a cigar. As Miguel approached, he heard the caballero call out to the victim: "Now will you clear out, leave the country entirely?"

"Si, senor," said the man. "I will if you buy my sheep, cattle and horses."

"Give him ten more," ordered the caballero. "One for Juan." Whack came the willow on the poor fellow's bleeding back. "One for Santiago" (another whack). "One for Diego" (more) "One for Jose." (again). "One for Pedro, son cinco, otra vez (that's five, one more time)."

He started again: "One for Juan, cuatro par pelon (four for good measure)."

Andres Pico

The victim meanwhile was screaming in agony. Juan raised his arm to take a turn but was unable to strike another blow, for a hitherto unseen—and alarmingly large—observer had seized him and sent the vaquero skittering along the ground as if thrown by a catapult.

The "Convento" building of the San Fernando Mission, as it appeared at the time it was used as a home by Andres Pico.

The remaining vaqueros fled to their horses as though the devil himself had risen from the ground. As for the dashing caballero, he had to struggle to rein up his horse and straighten himself in the saddle. Before the caballero was settled enough to speak, Miguel had cut the bound man loose.

"Diablo!" the caballero exclaimed. "De donde vienes?" (The devil, where did you come from?)

"I may be a devil, but not so much I can stand to see a man treated in such a manner," answered Miguel.

"Well, then, if not the devil, who are you?"

"I am a stranger in this land," Miguel explained, "a Basque. I am on my way to the rancho Tapo, where I am to be the new foreman. If I have been too officious in interfering here, please excuse me. I am new in this region and forgot myself."

The caballero looked intrigued. "You are a brave, handsome fellow. I like you," dismounting. "Why don't we go inside to tomar algo (drink something). He looked back with contempt as the lacerated and

Andres Pico bought the San Fernando Mission, and used the Convento building as his home. The artist shows a view from the wall of the building looking out through the arches toward the fountain which still stands, in a park across the street from the Mission.

newly liberated man put on his shirt. "Ah, Sin Verguenza (Shameless One), you can thank this Basquo Grande (Big Basque) for saving your hide. Yes, I will buy you out—but only on one condition. You must leave this country! I will not only purchase your cattle and your squaw, I will give them to this fellow who saved both of us—you from more stripes and me from further dishonor in so demeaning myself." Then to the ranch cook: "Give Menendez his breakfast and a bottle of aguardiente to cheer him on his way home."

Photograph by Ray Phillips.

Leonis' barn in 1947—taken from Valley Circle Blvd. Castle Peak in the background. the ruins of the Leonis' house are barely visible beyond the fence just to the left of the barn. The barn was demolished by developers in the 1960's, the entire little valley filled in; the entire area shown in the picture, except for the steep hillside, completely filled with houses.

He turned to Miguel: "I am Andres Pico, I am the law here,[8] and this miserable gachupin[9] has been squatting among my Indians and putting mischief into their poor heads. He makes servants and fools of the men, and worse with the women. I act not for my cattle or my pasture but for the protection of these honest well-meaning Indians. Why not buy him out, Basquo Grande? I will lend you the money. Settle down here and be my neighbor; be my friend. You can always count on Andres Pico."

Photograph by Ray Phillips.

The same scene as in the previous photograph, but taken in January, 1992. All traces of Rancho El Escorpion have been obliterated.

General Pico lived at the former mission in San Fernando, where he was lord paramount. At the time he also controlled Cahuenga, which in Mission times had been a dependency of the mother mission.[10] Pico explained that he and his five outriders had spent the previous night in Los Angeles and then galloped to Cahuenga, where they stopped for a cup of coffee.

The old Californio treated Miguel as though he were a distinguished stranger, furnishing him with a horse and saddle. "I will send a vaquero to Tapo for it later," he told him.

Menendez ate his breakfast, drank the aguardiente and mounted his horse. He and Miguel then took the Santa Barbara road, that being the best and nearest to El Escorpion.

On the way Menendez became increasingly communicative. He informed Miguel that he was a Spaniard by birth and a deserter from the Spanish army in the Philippines—that he came to California in the gen-

Los Encinos State Park.

Don Vicente is mentioned as getting sheep from Leonis' herds! His ranch was just east of Leonis's. The ranch house still stands, as a California state park.

eral rush for gold and had lived two years in Los Angeles, where he found himself an Indian girl named Espiritu, a daughter of Odon.[11] From Menendez, Miguel learned that Odon was owner of the rancho El Escorpion, four square leagues in size.[12] Menendez indicated that he had been residing with his Indian friends for the last two years, and that he owned 500 head of sheep, 30 head of horned cattle and 20 horses. Andres Pico was jealous of his influence with the San Fernando Indians, he said, and "that is all there is to it."

"Even so," he said, "I will have to sell out and leave the country."

Three leagues farther, the two travelers reached the ranch known as Los Encinos.[13] They drew rein in front of the casa of the hospitable Don Vicente de la Osa, owner of this beautiful one-league ranch. Great springs of fresh water, and mineral water as well, burst forth from the sloping plains. The men stood beneath the overhanging branches of the great live oaks—for there was a magnificent grove at the time, from which came the name of the ranch, "los encinos" meaning "live oaks."

Menendez thought a warm sulphur bath would benefit his deteriorated condition of health and, having obtained Don Vicente's permission, he disrobed and plunged into the smoking, seething, sulphurous mud and luxuriated for a full half an hour. Then, having washed himself in clean water and donned his clothes, he declared himself cured of whatever ills he had brought with him.

"I feel as lithe and active as a maromero (rope dancer)," he asserted. They continued their journey and arrived in the cool of the mid-afternon at El Escorpion, where they presented themselves to old Odon.

El Escorpion is the site of a prehistoric Indian town.[14] It is a beautiful nook in the corner of the mountains—with high rocky crags in the background, lovely grass-covered hills and a grand park of oaks in the foreground. On the right side and on the left are isolated buttes. From a gentle slope of fertile plain burst forth a variety of mineral springs, and also other springs of cold, sparkling, clear, fresh water. The foot of the slope had a flat bottom covered with a dense copse of green willow, and near the springs toward the Escorpion encinal (park) was the house of Odon.

The Indian's family consisted of an old and wrinkled wife and two buxom, good-looking daughters, Espiritu and Marcelina. Odon also had a son, a strapping fellow rigged out in the costume of a California vaquero.[15] The girls were not so dark in complexion as the pure Indian blood of Odon and his wife would suggest, and among knowing old ones of the village it was whispered that Spanish blood had been infused into the Odon family in the persons of Espiritu and Marcelina. In fact, Marcelina chose to ignore the family name of her father, Chijulla, and assumed the more aristocratic-sounding appellation of Marcelina Villa. Espiritu stood by the honor of her family, however, and called herself Espiritu Chijulla. In fact, all considered themselves Chijullas save and except the lofty Marcelina.

Several Indian families lived in comfortable adobe tule-roofed houses contiguous to that of Odon, forming a pretty and picturesque village. On a level mesa, the Indians cultivated and irrigated patches of beans, corn, melons and chiles. A field of about two hundred acres of wheat, property of the thrifty Odon, was located on the plain to the south as one journeyed to Calabasas, Virgines and, Conejo, all ranches in the direction of the sea coast. So thrifty was Odon that he had the monopoly of seed wheat for the Americans who began farming operations in the San Fernando valley during in the early fifties.[16]

Miguel delivered his message from Pierre Abadie and was given a most cordial reception. He was made comfortable as an honored guest and his horse was cared for.

As for Menendez, he was now at home and happy to get back, even with a pretty well tanned hide. He soon sought a second sulphur bath.༼

Endnotes

1. According to the map in W.W. Robinson's *Los Angeles From the Days of the Pueblo*, Marchessault Street no longer exists. It formerly ran in a north-south direction immediately east of the plaza. Upper Main Street, later renamed North Spring Street, met Marchessault just northeast of the Plaza Church. (p. 8)

2. "Tendajon" is a local-region corruption of the Spanish word "tienda"— meaning shop or store. It might be that "tendajon de la campana" was a variation of the term "tienda de campana," which means tent. (See *The American Heritages's Larousse Spanish Dictionary,* p.272). Bell's explanation is very plausible, however. In *The Decline of the Californios,* Leonard Pitt noted that in Los Angeles during the 1850s scarcely any house stood out of earshot of the plaza church bell, which served as the town's alarm system as well as a call to devotion. (p. 121)

3. In 1859 there were six hundred French people—one-fifth of the town's population—living in Los Angeles. In his book *Annals of Los Angeles 1769-1861,* J.Gregg Layne described the pueblo's French quarter as occupying the former site of Juan Domingo's vineyard, from Los Angeles Street to the river and between Aliso and First streets. (pp. 82-83) (Also, see map of old Los Angeles in *Los Angeles From the Days of the Pueblo*, p.8)

4. Concerning Mascarel's domestic arrangements, in *Le Guidea Francais De Los Angeles Et Du Sud De La Californie*, a reference is made that Mascarel joined the pueblo's small company of foreign volunteers to aid the invading Americans "although (he was) just married to Senorita Lugo, a descendant of the old Alvarado family of San Juan Capistrano." This event occurred approximately 1846.(p.23) In Mascarel's will, dated September 16, 1899, among his listed heirs are his children by the Indian woman Cerilda: Sylvester, Constance, Hortense and Maria Concepcion. The will also names a wife, Jesus Feliz, whose grave marker is located next to his in Calvary Cemetery.

5. Miguel Leonis' birth certificate from Cambo-les-bains indicates he was born on February 15, 1822. This would have made him 35 in May, 1857.

6. Rancho Tapo was in Ventura County, actually. Since it is on the other side of the Santa Susana Pass, from Los Angeles one would reach it by crossing the present-day community of Chatsworth.

7. Cahuenga is the name of a former Indian village in a hilly region now known as Hollywood.

8. Andres Pico (1810-1876) was a member of a prestigious Californio family—the younger brother of Pio Pico, last governor of California under Mexican rule. As a military man, Andres distinguished himself in battle against the Americans, particularly when he defeated the U.S. Cavalry led by General Kearney at San Pasqual (1846). In 1847 Pico represented the Republic of Mexico in its formal surrender to Colonel Fremont in the treaty at Cahuenga.

In *Reminiscences of a Ranger,* Horace Bell marveled at Pico's masterful handling of the treaty—for the Californios' 40-some men in reality had very few arms with which to make a stand. In the process of surrendering to Fremont, Pico verbally maneuvered some very liberal terms. In Bell's words, the "great humorist" Don Andres Pico was "throwing dust in (Fremont's) eyes as to the re-occupation of Los Angeles" when he induced him to make a treaty and bind the United States to the pardon of all Mexican officers involved. The truth was, unbeknownst to Fremont, Kearny had already taken the city two weeks earlier and these same Mexican officers had violated their parole to make this stand. (1927, p. 349)

9. In *The Decline of the Californios,* Leonard Pitt defined the term "gachupin" as meaning "Spanish settler." He further noted that in California the word took on an additional connotation: "monarchist." (p. 309)

10. When Andres Pico's brother Pio was the last governor of California under Mexican rule, among his last acts as governor was the distribution of huge tracts of public land to his friends and relatives. According to W.W. Robinson (1966), in 1847 the governor sold the former mission at San Fernando (former because all missions had been secularized during the Mexican period) to Eulogio de Celis, a family friend. This ex-Mission land grant took up the greater portion of the San Fernando Valley—some 116,000 acres—which Gov. Pico sold for $14, in order to raise cash for the Californios' stand against the Americans.

The new owner de Celis remained in Los Angeles and never did live on the ranch. His friend Andres Pico did, however, maintaining his residence in the mission itself and running the ranch under provision of the lease given him in 1845 by the Mexican government. In 1853 de Celis went to Spain and never returned. Andres continued to run the ranch for the de Celis heirs, eventually buying a half interest in it for $15,000.

11. According to court testimony by Jose Mascarel, as reported by the *Los Angeles Times* (May 22, 1891, page 2), Jose Antonio Menendez was a

Spaniard and one-time ranch foreman for Andres Pico at San Fernando. Mascarel testified during a contest of Miguel Leonis' will that Espiritu had lived with Menendez in 1853 or 1855. It appears that Menendez was an American citizen. In a preemption claim for 130 acres of public land in San Fernando, dated December 7, 1854, he stated he was a naturalized U.S. citizen.

12. Menendez exaggerated. The Mexican grant for El Escorpion stipulated one-half of a square league—a league being approximately three miles. The original survey was measured incorrectly, effectively reducing the size of the grant to one-quarter of a square league, and for many years thereafter the exact dimensions of the Escorpion Ranch were subject to intense dispute.

13. Rancho Los Encinos had been granted by Governor Pio Pico in 1845 to three Indians: Ramon, Francisco and Roque. Their interests were passed by deed to Vicente de la Osa, who built an adobe house near the springs, which still exist. Los Encinos was named after a large stand of evergreen oak trees, a spot first visited by Spain's Portola expedition (1769). During de la Osa's time, the site was a popular stopping place for travelers enroute to and from Los Angeles.

Almost destroyed by subdividers in the 1950's, the area right around the adobe and the lake formed by the springs was turned into a state park. It is just east of Ventura Boulevard and Balboa.

14. In his monograph, *El Escorpion: From Indian Village to Los Angeles Park,* Chester G. Cohen credited the earliest recorded mention of Escorpion to an entry in the Santa Barbara Presidio journal, dated September 17, 1783. Escorpion was the name the area had been dubbed by Spanish soldiers. Indians called their village Huwam. (p.2) According to Indian researcher Bob Edberg in his unpublished manuscript "History of the Rancho El Escorpion at the Mouth of Bell Canyon," in the year 1850 approximately one-quarter of the Los Angeles city

and county Indian population were residents of the Chumash village of Huwam, situated on El Escorpion land. The rancho's adobe structures had been constructed directly on the site of the old village, at the entrance to Bell Canyon on the north side of the creek. (p.2)

15. Federal census records for 1880 indicate that Odon had a third daughter, Maria Dolores. When Espiritu was baptized at San Fernando on April 25, 1820, her father Odon was listed as a soapmaker for the mission.

16. In a Mexican land grant dated 1845, Odon was one of three Indians on the original title to the rancho known as El Escorpion. The other two do not figure in Horace Bell's story. They were Urbano (Odon's son-in-law) and Urbano's son Manuel. In the U.S. Census of 1850, a fourth co-owner had appeared, Joaquin Romero, a non-Indian.

5

Rancho El Escorpion—Menendez
Andres Pico—Espiritu

iguel was perfectly enraptured by the grandeur and beauty of of El Escorpion. After sharing a repast of tortillas, coffee, stewed beef and beans—a good, square, honest, and appetizing meal—Odon invited his guest to view his domain from a high point.[1]

Pointing east toward the Encino, Odon indicated that its great grove of oak trees aligned with the eastern boundary of El Escorpion. A league (about three miles) or more to the south of the Indian settlement was the low range of mountains that formed El Escorpion's southern edge. On the west stood rugged, craggy, cavernous mountains. On the north, a promontory of smooth and grassy hills projected three miles east, directly from the mountain base into the plain. The northern base of this promontory marked El Escorpion's northern edge, the boundary between it and the lands of the Mission San Fernando.

It was Odon's understanding that El Escorpion measured twelve by four miles—forty-eight sections of land as measured by the United States government. The grant made by Governor Pio Pico, however, in a document dated August 7, 1845, called for only one and a half square leagues—a claim that nevertheless was confirmed on October 11, 1852.[2]

"Here is a ranch capable of maintaining at least thirty thousand head of sheep," Miguel thought.

Odon was then about seventy years old, a descendant of an Indian named Cahuenga who had dominated the San Fernando valley at the time of the first coming of the mission fathers. The warlike Cahuenga had been converted by the kind and gentle treatment of Father Junipero Serra, and he gave all of his energy, influence and strength toward the building of the San Fernando Mission.[3]

During this period, there were only two Indian settlements in the San Fernando valley, Escorpion and the Cienega de la Mission, located west of the Mission proper and the source of its water supply. Rogerio, the old-time mission blacksmith, was the "head man" of this settlement.[4]

By the time Odon and Miguel returned to the house, the small herds belonging to Menendez had been driven to their corrals— sheep, cattle and horses, each in separate folds. Menendez invited Miguel to inspect the stock and proposed to sell them to him. He would take a thousand dollars for the lot. "A good bargain," thought Miguel, because at that time sheep were worth two dollars a head, horned cattle about twenty dollars, and horses also twenty. It would have been a fair price for the sheep alone, making the cattle and the horses come as gratuities.

Miguel declined to make the purchase, however, on the grounds that he had engaged himself for a year with Pierre Abadie at the Tapo. Since Menendez wanted to sell immediately, as he intended to leave the country, he suggested to Miguel that the stock would be perfectly safe in the charge of Odon. "I will even throw in the girl as pelon," he said, nodding his head at Espiritu.

At that point Odon suggested that he was indeed willing to be responsible for the stock should Miguel wish to purchase them. Odon was pleased at the prospect of change—of ridding the rancheria of Menendez—and, in any case, he had formed a liking for Miguel. He would be responsible for the stock, he said, and their grazing could be for free. Miguel decided to lay the matter over for a few days, committing himself only to return to Escorpion the Sunday after next to give his final answer. In the meantime, he intended to continue on his way, under the direction of an Indian guide, and report for service at Tapo.

From 1905 watercolor by E. S. Fenyes in the Southwest Museum.

The home of Juan and Espiritu Menendez, in the northeastern potion of Rancho El Escorpion, before the arrival of Miguel Leonis. Note that by 1905 the right side of the adobe had disappeared.

The conversation was still in progress when Espiritu approached, distributing cigarettes with a brazier of coals, and she was invited to join in the discussion. Asked by Menendez what she thought of the change—that he would go away, Miguel would buy his stock and she would be transferred to Miguel—she responded "Esta bien (that's fine)." For the time being, the matter was settled.

Taking Miguel aside, Menendez elaborated on Espiritu's virtues. "When I came to Los Angeles, four or five years ago, Espiritu was the property of a French baker at Los Angeles.[5] The baker worked for Mascarel. I played monte[6] with this baker and won all of his money and then he proposed to put up Espiritu against fifty dollars. The result was that I won her and I have had her ever since. A most excellent girl she is—a great worker and very smart. She has more sense than all the other Indians put together—unless it is the wise old Odon himself, of course.

47

Espiritu will take the very best care of your stock if you leave them with her. Just see what an opportunity this is for you! Think how this stock will increase within a year! You can make additions to it and in a short time you will be a rich man, especially if you stay in good graces with Andres Pico. I got him down on me and so I am ruined. Now I must get out of here."

"It was my fault that I got Andres down on me," Menendez went on. "Being a Spaniard, I put on too much style. When I came to this country I held myself above the native Californians, but soon I found that they held themselves far above me. Why, do you believe it, when I journeyed from ranch to ranch in this country, these stuck-up barbarians would not permit me to sit at the table with them?! They would send me to the kitchen to mess with their Indian cooks. And they called me what they call all Spaniards, 'Gachupin.'"

"What is the meaning of that word?" queried Miguel.

"It comes from 'Capuchin.' You know that the Philippine Islands are full of Capuchin friars—well, these friars have an evil repute, one that has poisoned Mexicans from all over Mexico and California against Span- iards, especially those coming from Manila. A Capuchin is an unwel- come immigrant in all of Spanish America. So I have had a hard time of it. I am a Spaniard. I am, from their point of view, a Capuchin, and they just hate me for it. If I can get out of this country, I will go to the Sand- wich Islands—where I will be rid of them and their Injuns and high- toned caballeros. Greasers! Now, that is what the Americans call Mexi- cans and Californios alike—greasers. When first I was insulted with the word Capuchin I would retort 'greaser.' Invariably I would get knocked down, so I could not even talk back."

While the two were thus engaged in conversation, a very young boy came toddling along and Miguel inquired whose son he was.

"That is Juan . . . Menendez, I guess, though I am not so very sure of it. Espiritu is the mother—I know that. Perhaps I am the father, quien sabe? Take the cattle, Miguel, and you can have the mother and the boy also. Think what a start you will have made. Well, buenos noches, caballero, I am going to sleep."

The next morning, bright and early, Miguel was provided with a good breakfast and, together with his Indian guide, he continued on his journey to Tapo. He arrived early in the afternoon without further incident. Abadie was present at the ranch and and at once instructed Miguel on his duties and introduced him to the servants and sheep herders. On the following day Miguel was left master of the situation, Abadie having returned to Santa Barbara, where he lived like a grandee.℘

Endnotes

1. This is very likely the point known today as Castle Peak, which was located near the rancho's adobes.

2. Rancho El Escorpion lay in the far west end of the San Fernando Valley, a section later renamed Platt Ranch. According to Chester G. Cohen in his monograph on El Escorpion, the original 1845 survey made by Juan Sepulveda, assistant mayor-judge of Los Angeles, indicated the following landmarks (and their contemporary equivalents): northwest corner: the foot of a hill (near the present-day intersection of Valley Circle and Bell Canyon boulevards); northeast corner: a point in the plain of San Fernando where a landmark was placed (near Sherman Way at Woodlake Avenue); southeast corner: a low hill in the plain of San Fernando where an oak was placed as a landmark (Calvert Street west of Woodlake Avenue); southwest corner: a stake placed at the Canada de Encinos (Calvert Street west of Valley Circle Boulevard). (p.4)

3. While there may have existed an Indian named Cahuenga, the remainder of Bell's description is at best fanciful. For one thing, Father Serra

spent most of his life in northern California, not the San Fernando Valley. Also, in recent years history revisionists have seriously questioned this stereotypical view of the mission system's "kind and gentle" treatment of Indians.

4. Rogerio Rocha was one of 40 Indians whose name appears on an old (1843) grant for San Fernando Mission land. He is known to have lived upon and cultivated the section known as the Cienega (Spanish for swamp or marshland).

5. Bell may have got this information directly from Jose Mascarel's testimony during the court case contesting Miguel Leonis' will (reported by the *Los Angeles Times* on May 22, 1891, p.2). The French baker Menendez mentioned probably was Andre Maneau, a Frenchman whose name appears in accounts of that period from *Le Guide Francais De Los Angeles* (p.28). Mascarel testified in court that he and Maneau had been business partners in a bakery, and that he lived nearby and visited Maneau's house often. According to Mascarel, Espiritu lived with Maneau for several years, until they had a row and she went to live with her mother. He further testified that she was living wih a Spaniard named Menendez in about 1853 or 1855.

6. Monte was a card game popular in Mexico and California.

6

Rancho Tapo—Colonel Pacheco
Pierre Domec

Little novelty is found at a sheep ranch—where monotony is the general rule—although at Tapo this was not entirely so. Tapo was a typical California ranch of the day. It belonged to the rich and aristocratic Noriega family of Santa Barbara, and was a farm as well as a sheep ranch. There were vineyards, wine vats and presses, olive groves, orchards of deciduous fruits, fields and fields of corn, beans, pumpkins, squashes, melons, and the everpresent patch of chile peppers.

The ranch house was large and well-appointed. It had a good kitchen, with a Mexican range that was a great improvement over the cooking facilities at Mascarel's homestead in Los Angeles. This range consisted of a pair of parallel rows of bricks, covered by a roof of flat shale rock through which holes had been cut for the placement of pots, kettles and bake pans.

All the workers at the ranch were Indians except for the majordomo, who had less authority than that now bestowed on Miguel. Tapo's majordomo was an odd character—a careful, intelligent, educated Mexican who was energetic but greatly given to the imbibement of aguardiente. This necessitated many visits to the ranch on the part of Abadie, causing him much annoyance. Being wealthy, Abadie greatly enjoyed the sweet life of Santa Barbara and the company of his blooming

Mexican wife. She had been a widow— fair, fat and forty—with landed possessions and cattle interests when this lively son of Gaul married her.

Tapo's majordomo gloried in the title of colonel, calling himself Colonel Don Andres Larios y Pacheco. He was as tall as Miguel, erect and stately, of dark complexion and looking more Moorish than Indian. The gallant Pacheco was then about forty years of age and claimed to have been a full colonel in the Mexican army. He had fought at San Jacinto as a captain. At Monterey he did battle as a major, then at Buena Vista as a colonel. He greatly lamented his lowered status, reduced now to majordomo at a California sheep ranch. An astute man was the colonel—and a great storyteller besides, although he scorned to lower himself to recount his old-time escapades and military adventures to the Indians who surrounded him. When Abadie visited the ranch, however, the hairs of his head would be made to stand on end by the long military narratives spun out by Colonel Pacheco.

On the day following his arrival, Miguel reviewed the efficiency and order of the entire premises. Everything was in disarray. At the end of each day, the ten or twelve thousand head of sheep were driven in from the fields and enclosed in small corrals for the night. Then, the following morning, after a breakfast hour convenient for the workers, the sheep were sent out again to graze. In truth, the habits of the herders were slothful. Sheep were permitted to stray, often becoming prey to coyotes and other predatory animals—mountain lions, for instance.

Tapo's irrigating ditches had been permitted to grow full of weeds, so that when a vineyard or a grain field was irrigated, only about half the water reached its destination, the remainder being wasted along the way. The season for irrigation did not start until the month of June, at which time the bare ground was irrigated for the purpose of planting grain crops—preparing the land, as it were, first for the plow and then for the seeding.

The cook was boss of the kitchen, and a heavy-set Indian woman was the housekeeper, with several Indian girls acting as roustabouts, assistants to the cook and to the housekeeper. At Tapo, everyone seemed to do as much or as little as he or she pleased, and the sheep showed strong evidence of neglect. Miguel set his mind to work on bringing about some major reforms.

The first thing he did was notify all hands that they must be up at four o'clock in the morning. This was an astonishing piece of business: getting up at four o'clock in the morning was unheard of. At half past three early the next day, Miguel was up and among them, routing them out.

"Coffee at daylight," he instructed the Indian cook. "Your sheep must be out on pasture lands before the sun rises," he told each of the herders.

There was, on an average, one herder assigned to each thousand sheep, and the groups were all sent out together. The herders were allowed to take only their coffee; breakfast would be sent to them on the pasture grounds. Miguel also issued orders that the sheep were not to be returned at the close of the day until he himself had inspected them. The very next day, all the Tapo sheep were separated into six herds.

A thorough renovation of the house also took place. Work horses were inspected, harnesses repaired and cleaned up, the blacksmith shop put in order and all wagons, plows, harrows and pruning hooks overhauled, inventoried and arranged in order of use. The large barn where these things were stored was cleaned and whitewashed, inside and out. The wine cellars were put in order and one month later, when Abadie visited the ranch, he was astonished by the perfect order and system that prevailed. Everything looked neat. The fences and hedges had been repaired and trimmed, and everything was kept in its place. In a short space of time, Miguel had brought about a revolution, an achievement that utterly astounded the ranch's proprietor.

Even Colonel Pacheco had become orderly and useful. He was allotted a daily allowance of aguardiente and his duties clearly marked out. Perhaps because of his military training, Pacheco readily submitted himself to the discipline imposed by Miguel, whom he viewed as his superior by virtue of his employ and by natural endowment—both of which the colonel was quick to acknowledge.

The ranch sheep were suffering from sarna (Anglaise scab). This Miguel attributed to their close confinement in crowded corrals every night. So he separated the sheep into six herds, each with its two Indian herders, each with his own dog—though at that time they did not have the trained sheep dogs afterward introduced into this country as valuable assistants to the human herder.

It may be accurately said that at this time the range for Abadie's sheep was utterly without limit. His sheep could graze on the entire Simi ranch and the Santa Clara river bottoms. The Tapo itself was a valley contiguous to—and distributing its waters into—the Santa Clara river.

To the astonishment of the herders, Miguel required them to bunch the sheep in favored locations at nightfall rather than bring them back to the ranch corral for the night. Since there were two men assigned to each herd, they had an easy time of it. One would go to the ranch and bring the meals out while the other cared for the sheep, and it was surprising to observe the improvement this system of grazing made on the general herds. At daylight the herds were started out on their grazing rounds and permitted to move at will all day. The sheep could go to their favored watering places and bunch together in the shade during the heat of the day. While this made the work easier for the herders, they no longer could enjoy the society of other workers and visitors to the ranch—no more smoking, drinking, dancing, gossiping and playing cards as they had formerly spent the evenings after the labors of the day.

Whenever Abadie visited, Colonel Pacheco spoke to him in glowing terms of the new boss. "What a wonderful man is this Don Miguel Leonis!" exclaimed the colonel to his patron. "He is clearly a general by nature—were he in Mexico where I came from, and a soldier, he would have made a great general. Ah, my old friend and patron, his excellency the President Santa Ana, he would have recognized such merit! He would have made him a major-general after his first campaign. If the president had had such men as you have here—when he invaded Texas—the disaster at San Jacinto would never have happened. I was only a captain then, and what miserable imbeciles we had to lead on that campaign, as commanding officers. Why, they just went to sleep. They permitted those dastardly Texans to come in and kill and scatter us like sheep. If it had only occurred a few days before! The evening before the battle the president sent for me and he said, 'Captain Don Andres, I have observed your gallantry; you are a very brave man. You are a very orderly man, you are a natural military genius, Captain Pacheco, and I propose immediately to promote you to a colonelcy and make you chief of my staff."

"I was elated by this recognition from Mexico's greatest hero—but then I didn't get the promotion. The next day the Texans took us, and the whole world knows the disgraceful result. Afterward, however, when the gringos[1] crossed the Rio Grande and Santa Ana was marshaling his armies to repel the invasion, one day he again observed me. He had forgotten who I was—had supposed me killed at San Jacinto—all of which time I had been serving as a captain and had got up to the rank of major.'

"One day immediately after review, an aide-de-camp ordered me to report at the presidential marquee. Ah! a great man was Antonio Lopez de Santa Ana. And he said to me, 'Colonel.'

"I made the salute and stood at attention. I said, 'Major, if you please, Mr. President.'

"'No, it is colonel. Your rank is major now, is it? In what line of service?'

"'Infantry,' I answered.

"You are now a colonel of cavalry, sir. Give me your full name."

"Andres Larios y Pacheco," I answered.

Turning to his secretary, he said, "Enter the name, and tomorrow morning issue a general order promoting Major Andres Larios y Pacheco of the Twenty-second Infantry of the line, to colonel of the Fourteenth Regiment of Lanceros."

"And such was I, patron, at the battle of Buena Vista. Ah, what a matanza (massacre) that was. I think we must have killed about ten thousand gringos at that battle, and we only lost about two thousand. We would have killed the last gringo of that army had it not been, in the afternoon of the second day's battle—when my regiment was away after the last of the scattering gringos—that I was unexpectedly recalled. An express message had come from Mexico City with the announcement of a revolution, and I was ordered to held my regiment in readiness to march as the presidential escort. Our army, then engaged in finishing up the gringos, was drawn off, faced about and marched in hot haste to the City of Mexico to quell that revolution. Ah, those traitors—those rascally revolutionists. Had they held their peace we could have slaughtered the last Yankee west of the Rio Grande. We would have crossed over, recaptured Texas and wiped out the disgrace of San Jacinto."

"Yes, we would have marched to the capital of Washington and there we would have dictated terms of peace, instead of having the gringos at a later day possess themselves of our beloved capital and wrest California and New Mexico from us as the conditions of peace and their retirement from our country. I was on the point of promotion to brigadier-general, but so humiliated was I at the mortification of my country that I broke my sword into pieces. I tore my uniform in shreds. I killed my war horse, and, in the garb of a common Mexican, I fled the country. So here I am in California, second in command of a sheep ranch. Ah, patron, patron, what humiliation is mine. Instead of marshaling the chivalry of Mexico in lines of battle and in squares for defense, I am mustering and marshaling a lot of dirty, sarna-infested sheep. Marshaling their herders—who have less sense than the sheep themselves—but, thank God, I have a captain over me. Ah, this Miguel! Give him a chance and he will be a great man."

Meantime, on the second Sunday as promised, Miguel returned to El Escorpion to keep his appointment with Odon and Menendez in respect to the purchase of Menendez' stock. The herds were brought to the corrals and counted. There were five hundred, also fourteen head of sheep, sixteen cows, most of which had young calves, fourteen mares, six geldings, four of which were broken to the saddle—the others were being ridden bare-back, with a halter, by Indian boys of the rancheria. A thousand dollars for the entire outfit! The trade was made and Miguel gave Menendez an order on Mascarel for a thousand dollars. Espiritu said she herself would take charge of the stock, and Odon promised his authority and assistance to see that everything went well. With that, Miguel prepared to leave for Tapo.

Just before he started, however, there appeared at the ranch a robust, ruddy-faced and muscular Frenchman. His name was Pierre Domec,[2] and he said he was in the business of burning limestone close by. With a sly wink at Miguel, Domec intimated that he was a suitor for the hand of Marcelina[3]—and that he was doing a pretty good business at burning lime, which he sent to Mascarel at Los Angeles. Mascarel then placed it on the market, lime being a great commodity at the time.

In fear that Miguel might get ahead of him, Domec soon pressed his suit for the hand of Marcelina, and the lovely Marcelina Villa became Marcelina Villa de Domec. To this day, the descendants of the Domecs and the Villas and the Odons still inhabit the mountain fastnesses in the regions of the Escorpion. As for Domec himself, he became a thorn in Miguel's side, as will be hereafter related.☙

Endnotes

1. A gringo is a foreigner, a greenhorn, a term especially applied to Anglo-Saxons, according to Leonard Pitt in his *Decline of the Californios*. He suggests a connection with a song U.S. armymen used to sing in Mexico, "Green Grow the Violets." (p.309)

In *Reminiscences of a Ranger*, Horace Bell explains the full California connotation of the term: "Gringo, in its literal signification, means ignoramus. For instance an American who had not yet learned to eat chili peppers stewed in grease, throw the lasso, contemplate the beauties of nature from the sunny side of an adobe wall, make a first-class cigar out of a corn husk, wear open-legged pantaloons with bell buttons, dance on one leg, and live on one meal a week. Now the reader knows what a terrible thing it was in early days to be a gringo." (p.49)

2. Pierre Domec came to Los Angeles in 1844 on Jose Mascarel's ship, a schooner named "La Joven Fanita." He had been picked up in Mazatlan by Captain Mascarel, Domec having been sent for from France by Louis Vignes, a French settler who had a winery in Los Angeles. (See biographical sketch of Mascarel, Southern California Historical Society Pioneer Register of Los Angeles—1899, p.285)

3. This is not quite how it was. Domec settled down with Maria Dolores, a third Chijulla sister, whom Bell never mentions. At the time of the story, Marcelina was married to an Indian named Urbano, one of the original title holders to El Escorpion.

4. According to Chester Cohen in his monograph on El Escorpion (1989): "The making of lime from the limestone deposits in the Simi Hills had been an industry in the western San Fernando valley since Huwam village became Rancho El Escorpion. In 1858 a number of Frenchmen took up the occupation there. Some of the quarries were on Rancho ex-Mission San Fernando land and were leased from Gen Andres Pico. Other quarries were on or near Rancho El Escorpion. The lime had a ready market in Los Angeles—for mortar in brick construction, for the process of tanning cowhides, and in sanitation."

The remains of a lime kiln that may well have been Domec's can be seen from the corner of Woolsey Canyon Road and Valley Circle Blvd., Chatsworth. They lie east across a field and on a slight rise, under a tin-roofed shed. The area is now part of the Chatsworth (dry) reservoir, owned by the Los Angeles Department of Water and Power.

7

Odon, Marcelina—The Domec Conspiracy

It might be here remarked that Menendez, after having sold Miguel Leonis all his cattle, horses and sheep, his "lares" and his "penates," departed for San Luis Obispo—his first halt on his way to San Francisco. He proposed to sail from that city to the South Sea islands, where the Capuchins were unknown. Feeling perfectly safe by having removed himself so far from the wrath of Andres Pico, Menendez took great delight in vituperating him, he missed no opportunity to heap maledictions and abuse upon the absent caballero's head.

Representatives of the Pico family were in San Luis Obispo, however, and General Andres Pico had been California's hero during the Mexican war. Andres being a jolly good fellow, brimful of gallantry and generosity, he was idolized by his countrymen in households from San Diego to Sonoma. Menendez did not know this. So, on one occasion while he entertained a host of good fellows in a San Luis Obispo cantina, Menendez began one of his verbal assaults on the character of Andres Pico—denouncing him as everything that was mean, contemptible and cowardly. A young Californian resented the imputations, took great offense, and confronted the Capuchin, with the result that Menendez was shot dead. This was in 1858, about one year after he left the Escorpion.

Domec took Marcelina to his tule-roofed adobe house about three months after Menendez sold his stock to Leonis. Miguel's frequent visits to the Escorpion caused a high degree of jealousy in Domec—for the Frenchman was anxious to control Odon and eventually acquire the Escorpion ranch, and become a stock magnate himself. Determined to cause mischief against Miguel, Domec went to Los Angeles to seek help. He went among the Basque people who had settled in the city and among those engaged as herders and sheep raisers on several ranchos. And somehow or other he got it into his head—that is, the information leaked out—that Miguel was a fugitive from the Basque country. Domec had letters sent to people in Miguel's homeland and was able to ascertain that Miguel indeed had been a smuggler in the Pyrenees, a chief among smugglers. He learned that in an encounter between Miguel's band of smugglers and the Spanish Customs guards, quite a number of the guards had been killed, for which reason Miguel had to be smuggled out of the country. So Domec had the information he needed.

All of these things he laid before his father-in-law Odon, warning him against allowing such a character about the Escorpion rancheria. Domec threatened the old Indian with the notion that the Spanish would seek Odon personally—that they would arrest him, deport him, and carry him back to Spain, where deservedly he would be hanged or shot.

Odon did not listen to Domec with profound respect. In fact, he did not like him. The old Indian had even objected to the thought of Marcelina marrying the man—but when it was hinted that Odon possibly was not the natural father of Marcelina, he dropped the matter. Allowed to do as she pleased, Marcelina chose to become the wife of the scheming Frenchman.

At the end of Miguel's term of service at Tapo, Abadie offered him a partnership in the sheep business if he would only continue on—but this Miguel declined, stating that he had already acquired a few sheep. With the money he had on deposit with Mascarel, the wages he earned during his one-year service at Tapo, and the arrangement made with Odon for pasturage on the Escorpion, Miguel felt confident that he was ready to go into business, independently and alone.

For that reason, when he came to draw his wages he preferred to take the $720 due him in sheep. He offered to pay a thousand dollars for

Adobe ranch house of the Leonis family at Rancho El Escorpion.

five hundred ewes, his wages plus the difference in cash—but so pleased was Abadie with Miguel's services that he told him to select the five hundred head of ewes out of his vast herds, to take them and call it even.

This done, Miguel transferred his flock of five hundred sheep to the Escorpion. He had a beginning. His original stock at the Escorpion had almost doubled in number, so the five hundred added to them made a splendid starter. Miguel settled down, bent on making a million dollars.

One of the first things that Miguel did for his new sheep was to prepare a special bath for them. He was determined that no sarna should exist among his flocks. On the sloping bench of a mountain spur was the beginning of a great spring of sulphur water, and immediately below this Miguel excavated the ground and built a great stone tank twelve feet deep. It was several yards in diameter, constructed of stone and cement, and the spring was permitted to run into and through it. On the ledge above the spring, Miguel placed a corral into which he would put his thousand or more sheep. In the morning they were let out on the side of corral that opened onto the tank. The sheep would rush out of the corral and fall into the bubbling sulphur water, where they would be helped out on the other side of the tank and they could go their way, clean and sarna-free.

Later, when Don Miguel Leonis had increased his sheep to forty thousand in number, there was no such a thing as sarna known among his various herds. To this day, that great bathing tank is a marvel. It is a curiosity and many wonder why and by whom it was constructed.[1]

Miguel built a house for Odon—a well-constructed and lime-plastered adobe house with a shingle roof. There Odon lived with his wife, and Miguel built another house for himself, and then another house. Afterward, he constructed a great two-story barn, with a painted-red shingle roof, all made of the finest construction of the day.

Miguel's stock multiplied with exceeding rapidity, and with every passing year the man known as El Basco Grande waxed richer and richer. He maintained a household, he had servants. Impatient of the shiftless habits of the Indians, he procured the services of the best of the Basque immigrants, paying them good wages and in return getting good service. Espiritu was his housekeeper.

Domec's ranch was situated about a league to the north, as one journeys from the Escorpion to the Santa Susana pass.[2] Domec was French but not Basque—and had collected about him several Frenchmen in the course of his lime-burning operations and his gathering of horses and cattle. Also working on his ranch were several Indians and a strapping, burly young native California Mexican named Manuel. With these men as his auxiliaries, Domec thought he could force an issue with Miguel Leonis. He determined to bring Odon into the fray by making trouble between the Indian and his favored son-in-law, the big Basque.

By hook or by crook the Frenchman had collected quite a herd of horses and a few cattle. It was easy to acquire horses in those days. A man watching for his opportunity could obtain a dozen or so mares at a time for trifles in money. The ranchero who needed money very badly—and had mares to spare—would sell them for cash at most any price.

As a result of Domec's natural animosity, his jealousy and his cupidity, trouble soon arose between himself and Miguel and Odon. The old Indian still maintained his liking for Leonis and an aversion to Domec. One of the Frenchmen employed by Domec was named Leude, another was Carmel.[3] Manuel, the Californian, Domec thought particularly useful to him because the young man was brash enough to do his bidding, however desperate the enterprise.

The year was now 1860. Marcelina harbored as great a dislike for Miguel Leonis as did her husband Pierre Domec—and she had little love for Odon, though she recognized him as her father because of an interest in the Escorpion ranch that might come to her by virtue of inheritance. But still, she considered herself Marcelina Villa, not Marcelina Chijulla.

One day she and Domec devised a plan by which they thought they could get the better of Leonis and bring him into disrepute. The plan was that they would corral Leonis' horses—and charge that the animals had trespassed on the Domec part of the Escorpion. Domec claimed the land north of the three-mile promontory, a point Odon said was the northern boundary of the El Escorpion ranch. The Domecs insisted that the promontory actually divided the ranch in the middle, hence they claimed dominion over the land north of the promontory and conceded to Leonis the uncontested use of all that lay south of that projection. So the plan was made that, upon the first occasion Leonis' horses wandered north of the promontory, they would be driven into the Domec corral. Damages would be claimed from Leonis and, if he attempted to take his horses back, the Domecs would be ready to defend their premises, with rifles and revolvers if necessary.

To this prospect, Leude, Carmel and Manuel pledged their support. Counting himself, Domec had four fighting men at his disposal, and he had three or four Indians upon whom he thought he might rely in case of emergency. He could muster almost ten rifles. But the plan was never consummated—because Leonis did not permit his stock to graze north of the promontory. He recognized all of that land as the property of Andres Pico, ignoring the Domecs' pretentions altogether.

A secondary plan was to use the cunning and enterprise of Manuel—Manuel El Diablo as he was known—wherein he would watch for an opportunity to drive Leonis' horses around the point onto Domec's domain and into the corral. An adroit and enterprising fellow was this Manuel. He was then about twenty years of age and belonged to the notorious Dominguez family. He was an expert vaquero, a skilled cattle lifter, and rumor had it he was a most expert sheep raiser, even though he had no herds. The sheep he "raised" were instantly turned over to a patron, who paid him immediately.

Jule Dreux, one of Leonis' men and a Basque, happened to see Manuel drive the Leonis horses from their pasturage, and he at once notified his master. Dreux was ordered to proceed to the Domec ranch in quest of the animals and bring them back. When he got arrived, however, he found the Leonis horses corraled and several of Domec's people swaggering around with their revolvers strapped on. Dreux stated his errand and was informed that, as the horses had been trespassing on Domec property, a price would have to be paid for their release. When Dreux claimed he had seen the horses driven away from Leonis' pastures and that the Mexican Manuel was the man who did it, Manual drew his revolver and vituperated his accuser as a falsifier. He further threatened to riddle Dreux's body with bullets unless he immediately departed the premises.

This Dreux did immediately, and he reported his story to Leonis. Miguel called over another man, Charles Leboubon, and told the two to arm themselves, they were going to get the horses. In less than half an hour the three arrived at the corral. Pierre Domec stood at the corral gate, armed with a double-barreled shotgun, while the others stood nearby with revolvers and rifles. Handing his revolver to Dreux, Miguel walked down to Domec and said "Cunado (brother-in-law)—I have come to take my horses home."

"Touch a bar of that corral gate and you are a dead man," was Domec's response.

In less than a half second, Leonis pounced on Domec like a blue jay on a June bug. Domec's shotgun was wrested from his hands and he himself was pitched thirty feet over the corral gate, where he fell among the astonished horses. Leonis thereupon quietly removed the bars, herded the horses out and told his two men to drive them home. He took back his revolver from Dreux and, keeping Domec's double-barreled shotgun, he mounted his horse. Driving the herd before them, the three went quietly home.

And so the old adage by Robert Burns came to pass: "The best laid plans of mice and men gang aft aglee." The Domec conspiracy was a flat failure—for they had attempted to bluff the wrong man. Where Domec had thought he had been spreading rumors about Miguel's past as a contraband king, now he was convinced of the truth of it.

When Domec found himself pitched into the corral, he had been utterly dumbfounded. Now he pulled himself together, straightened himself as best he could and shook the dust from his clothing. Surveying his dispirited retainers, he said "Que paso?"

"Quien sabe?" Manuel responded

By this time Marcelina had reached the corral, where she scornfully observed the sorry condition of her husband. "Que paso?" she exclaimed.

"Quien sabe," her husband answered.

Then followed a severe tongue-lashing from his disgusted better half, who said: "Senor Domec, I think it would be better for us to sell all our stock to El Basco Grande. Then we can move over to the Escorpion and work for him! Why didn't you fight him?! Why didn't you shoot him, as you said you would? What happened that he got away with the horses, when he had only two men while you had seven? Tell me! What is the matter, Pierre Domec?!"

"Quien sabe," came the old reply.

The episode was over for the present—but the wrath of Marcelina was yet to be appeased. Turning to her unhappy spouse she cried out:

"Coward, what happened to your shotgun?"

The doleful Domec replied, "Quien sabe?"

Then, turning the full fire of her anger upon Manuel, she shrieked: "Mongrel! Cur! what are you here for?"

"No se," came the morose reply.

"Ah! tan valiente (so valiant)! Outnumbering him eight to one and you still let the horses go! Sin Verguenzas (shameless ones), get out! Pierre Domec, begone. Find a hole in the mountain and crawl into it!" ᏻ

Endnotes

1. This certainly sounds like Bell was describing a real place. If so, it no longer exists.

2. Pierre Domec was squatting on land belonging to the ex-Mission San Fernando. Called the New Escorpion, the ranch where the Domecs lived overlapped the north corner of the ex-Mission land—approximately where the empty Chatsworth Reservoir stands today. Andres Pico tolerated their presence, so it was not a problem until the northern portion of the ranch was sold in 1877 and the new owners demanded rent. (Cohen, 1989, pp.20-21)

3. According to Cohen (1989), these two were Pierre Leude and Francois Carmel—two Frenchmen who were involved with Domec in an apparently unrelated 1860 court case against Charles Leboubon, a Frenchman who worked on the Escorpion for Miguel. (p.11-15)

8

Domec Loses—El Diablo's Conversion
Sheep Rustlers

omec was a wily, unscrupulous character—but in a negative way. As the old saying goes, "he lacked sand." He was
capable of undertaking very desperate ventures, but not of
carrying them through. Immediately, he regretted not
having placed Manuel instead of himself at the corral gate, for he had the
utmost confidence in Manuel's grit. Although the young fellow had
promise as a scoundrel of superlative degree, Manuel could be counted
upon to stand up and face the Devil if necessary.

As for Leude and Carmel, they clearly had little interest in
Domec's affairs other than the wages they earned burning lime. He was
hardly surprised by their lukewarm attitude toward the fight he had intended. The truth of it was, Domec fully intended for Leonis to be
killed—although he did not want to do it himself.

"What next?" he thought to himself dismally. He had lost face
with Marcelina—whose combination of Indian and Mexican blood
made her always ready for a fight. She was game to her backbone, and
Domec greatly feared to face her. He called Manuel to him, and they
retired to a secluded corner to discuss what to do.

"What do you think we should we do?" asked Domec.

"Go to Los Angeles and have them arrested."

"How can we? What did they do?"

Leonis Adobe Archives.

Pierre Domec and wife.

"Well, they did you up effectively, Senor Domec. And from the appearance of your clothes, the lameness of your walk and your skinned elbows that show for themselves, it seems to me you can say they did a good deal."

"Then why didn't you shoot him when he pitched me over the fence?"

Manuel shrugged.

"If we have them arrested," Domec mused, "I am afraid we couldn't make a good showing. I think the two Frenchmen might stand in with us, but those stupid Indians would be apt to tell the truth and then it would go badly for us."

"I will see that it does not go against us," said Manuel. "I know the judge at Los Angeles. We will go down together, but let me visit the judge beforehand. I know him. We call him 'El Tuerto' (one-eyed). He is an old-time gambler, now a justice of the peace. The Americans call him Blinker Bill, or something of the sort. I will see him first—but, before I go in to see him, Senor Domec, furnish me with a twenty-dollar gold piece. Once I have seen him, everything will be all right."

Keeping their own counsel, Domec and Manuel went the next day to Los Angeles. Manuel visited Blinker Bill, slipped the twenty-dollar gold piece into his hand, and told the story of the murderous assault—all from Domec's stand. The judge suggested that Domec file a complaint, which Domec did, charging Dreux and Leboubon with assault with intent to commit murder.

Nothing was said against Leonis in the complaint. Although Domec was angry with him, he thought he could better wreak his vengeance on the two hired men. These were accordingly arrested, brought to town and held to answer before his honor, Blinker Bill.

The constable who went to the Escorpion to serve the warrant assured Leonis that there was nothing in it, that he had made inquiry and it would not be necessary for Leonis to come to Los Angeles to defend his employees or even to be a witness. He ventured that the probabilities were that Dreux and Leboubon would be dismissed without examination.

Leonis took the precaution of sending a letter to Mascarel, however, in which he requested him to look out for the boys and see they were properly defended. Mascarel called in the lawyer Brent to defend

Joseph Lancaster Brent,
Julio Verdugo's legal counsel.

them. Not only were Dreux and Leboubon examined, they were remorselessly prosecuted—with Domec, Leude and Carmel testifying strongly against them. Manuel Dominguez remained at the ranch to keep the Indians in the background for fear they might let out the truth. The result was that Dreux and Leboubon were held to answer to the grand jury for an assault to murder Domec.

The two were indicted, brought before the Court of Sessions and tried. Once the Indians were brought in as witnesses, however, Domec's scheme—the whole conspiracy—was exposed, with the result that the two defendants were most honorably acquitted. Upon being honorably discharged, the defendants brought suit against Domec for malicious prosecution, and Domec was ordered to pay damages in the amount of two thousand dollars cash. He appealed the judgment to the Supreme Court of California, but the decision was affirmed and the profits from Domec's lime burning, plus the cattle he had, went to pay the bill. The horses and the cattle were levied upon and sold at auction, where Miguel Leonis bought them at his own price.

For verification of this warlike episode, the reader is respectfully referred to the 18th California Supreme Court Reports, page 83.

Where poor Domec was left humiliated and chastened by these events, Marcelina's response was one of wrath. She swore vengeance upon the whole outfit—upon the Basco Grande and all his retainers, upon her sister Espiritu, upon her father Odon—and she heaped countless anathemas on the heads of Domec and the hapless Manuel. Finally, she put her mind to work for some mischief of her own. Marcelina was a strong character. She had all the cunning of an Indian, a Mexican's capacity for malice and a Spaniard's for tenacity—all of which made her a person not easily dismissed.

Freakish incidents of nature have occurred—and still do—in California. For instance, during the pastoral epoch, cows were particularly odd creatures. Some rancheros' stock never increased at all, whereas those of a ranchero's neighbor multiplied in seemingly biblical proportions.

Don Nazario was a modern Jacob in that respect, as each of his cows had two, three or sometimes four calves tagging at its heels—while on an adjoining ranch Don Manuel's cows, or at least many of them, would go about calfless. So it was throughout southern and perhaps all of California in the good old times. An active and energetic, wide-awake ranchero would ride twenty miles in a night, and return home before daylight with a brace of suckling calves deftly slung across his saddle croup. His confidential vaqueros discreetly did likewise, and Don Nazario's horned cattle thereby multiplied in compound proportions.

Because Manuel Dominguez loved his soft wool mattress, with its clean linen sheets, and his morning nap—his cows often were bereft of their young. Of course, the situation of the neighboring dons, Nazario and Manuel, is only an example of how ranch cattle frequently increased in those old days. In those happy times, it was a rule that a man should never eat his own beef—for his ranch supply he must draw on some other ranchero's herd. A rancher who ignored this rule was not very successful in the cattle-raising business.

By the year 1860, Don Miguel Leonis had become a power in the regions of Escorpion, San Fernando, Calabasas and Virgines. He had kept on very friendly terms with his neighbor Don Andres Pico, who bestowed upon him a fine saddle horse, with trappings, twenty brood mares and wine from his vaults at the mission. Pico always remembered him with some of his best grape brandy. The fact is, the two became almost as close socially as compadres[1]—and the only reason they did not come together in such a relation is that neither one was married.[2]

71

Miguel's prodigious efforts, his disposition toward the Indians, and his tact in the management of his hired help combined to make the Escorpion one of the most beautiful ranches in southern California. A short three years after his arrival in Los Angeles, Leonis found himself the master of fully three thousand head of sheep, one hundred head of horned cattle, and forty or fifty horses. He believed he was well on his way to the coveted million dollars and felt confident that he would be able to procure this amount for the good Father Jean's noble purpose.

Miguel had acquired a goodly household. He was now an embryo grandee—with Indian servants, male and female, and Espiritu as his housekeeper. Surely the new settler, in these genial and prolific surroundings, was a man to be envied.

One day Dreux came to Leonis and reported that many of the rancho lambs seemed to be missing. Frequently he noticed a ewe minus its lamb, and then another and another.

Said Dreux,"I think perhaps a bear is getting into the herds."
An investigation on foot was ordered—and it was discovered that as many as a hundred lambs, as well as they could judge, were missing. In no manner could they account for such a great loss. The ranch was well-guarded against coyotes, and a bear entering a sheepfold would not be so selective as to pick out only lambs. A bear was more apt to go for full-grown sheep, for he could carry away the carcass and it would make a better meal. At the Escorpion, the ewes with lambs spent the night in a sleeping place a couple of hundred yards down the arroyo—in a sort of natural corral that was almost a cave indented in the side of the mountain. It looked very much like a volcano with a segment broken out. Near this was a long willow grove, which extended from the area above the house almost to the old crater-like corral below.

In tracking around, one of the Indians discovered a freshly made path through part of this willow bottom, which showed conclusively that some animal had come in and through the bottom in the direction of the ewes' sleeping place. They could not discern what kind of an animal it might be. The tracks were large—perhaps those of a bear—but only barely perceptible.

Dreux was sent to Los Angeles to purchase a great bear trap from Mascarel, and it was planted into the ground—in the willow grove and upon the pathway. Two nights after the men had set the trap, the herders were startled by a rumpus in the bushes. Away they went with their dogs after the intruder, and sure enough they came upon him. The creature had escaped, however. He had succeeded in loosening the chain from the tree to which it had been fastened, and was making his way with all rapidity possible, carrying the chain in one hand and dragging the trap, still fastened to his leg, after him.

The dogs reached him first and when the herders arrived, they carried the intruder—chain, trap and all—to the house of Don Miguel. A light revealed that the raider was none other than Domec's man, Manuel Dominguez. He was in a terrible state. A trap big enough for a grizzly bear is the wrong thing to fool with. It is as bad as a shark's jaws, and the wonder was that Manuel's leg had not been snapped off.

"Why, Don Manuel," Miguel observed, "Que hace aqui?" (What are you doing here?)

"Quien sabe?" came the guarded reply.

"I said, what are you doing here, sir?"

"Quien sabe?"

"Where were you going?"

"Oh, I was going to Calabasas."

"And what were you doing there in the willows?"

"Quien sabe?"

"What did you intend to do with the sack you had with you?"

"I didn't have any sack."

"It is still fastened over your shoulder! Now, what was it for? What were you going to do with it?"

"I was going over to Calabasas to get some sugar and coffee for Senor Domec."

"At midnight?"

"Si."

"Bring a rope and tie this fellow up. Now, take the sack off his shoulder and pull off his shirt. And get some willow switches. I am going to know something about this, Don Manuel!"

Manuel begged that first the trap should be released from his foot. This done, he was given a drink of aguardiente and then triced up to a cornice pole of the corridor. An Indian was ordered to give him a taste of the willow.

After a few stripes on his bare back, Manuel volunteered that, if all could be forgiven, he would tell the whole story.

"Yes, Don Miguel, I will give the whole thing away. I will be your servant, your slave—and I will do your bidding as long as I live and for as long as you need me."

"Well," said Miguel, "if you tell me the truth, I will forgive you—provided, as you say, you do my bidding hereafter. Otherwise, I will hang you by the neck until you are dead!"

Manuel thereupon called on all the saints in heaven to witness the honesty of his intentions, and he was taken into a room where a light was burning. Here he confessed that he had been stealing lambs every night for about two months, four or five lambs each night. He had several patrons who purchased the lambs, at twenty cents a head.

"Some I dispose of at the Encino. Other people at Calabasas also procure lambs from me. And if you will go over to our ranch tomorrow you will see a goodly herd there."

"What?" said Miguel. "The Domecs now raise sheep?"

"Oh, yes, they have quite a herd. Marcelina bought twenty-five ewes from Jeronimo Lopez about two months ago. And I don't know how it came about, Don Miguel, but each of those ewes has three or four lambs now—lambs just getting big enough to eat the little green grass and not pull very heavily on the stepmother."

Manuel led Dreux and the others to the place where he had tied his horse the night before, whereupon he told them his plan of operation. He would enter the sheepfold, snatch three or four lambs and put them into his shot-pouch sack, after which he would make his way back to his horse. By daylight, he would be perhaps twenty miles away, having earned an easy dollar for his night's work. It was a small business in its way, except the don often lifted a heifer or a colt for a little herd he was starting for himself. An enterprising young man was this Don Manuel.

After Manuel had made a full confession, stating he had stolen as many as two hundred fifty head of sheep, of all sizes and kinds, Leonis took him to Los Angeles. In front of the lawyer Brent, Manuel recounted his confession and Brent reduced it to writing with particular detail. A notary was called in and, with great formality, Manuel signed and swore to the truth of his statement. In this, he had incriminated several important sheep-raisers other than the Domec people. They included the the Virgines folk, those of Los Encinos, of Providencia (Burbank), Cahuenga (Hollywood), La Brea, and even north as far as San Francisquito, all had been peddled to by Manuel Dominguez—and all had received the lambs knowing them to have been stolen from Leonis.

After Manuel's confession had been duly sworn to and sealed by the notary, Leonis took it and said: "I am grateful to you, Senor Oso (Mr. Bear). You should add 'Oso' to your name. Here we sought to trap a bear and caught ourselves a caballero."

"For the love of God, Don Miguel, call me devil—I'd prefer it. Just don't forever remind me of this infernal mishap. I will be your slave and serve you faithfully. Please, just drop that part of it."

"Very well," replied Leonis, "I think I will call you Don Manuel, El Diablo. Now, Senor Diablo. As long as you keep still, do my bidding and help repair the wrong you have done me, this confession will be kept secret. However, if you refuse or fail to do the honest and fair thing, you will be turned over to the sheriff along with this confession. It should be enough to send you to the island for the remainder of your life. Is it not so, Senor Brent?"

"Absolutely so," Brent said. "And, Senor Diablo, if this should come to pass, I will take great pleasure in helping you on your way."

With impressive solemnity, Manuel Dominguez declared, "Sirs, my gratitude shall be eternal, my friendship everlasting; of whatever service I can be to Senor Leonis, he has only to order and I will obey—even to killing his enemies. While it is true I stole his sheep, I will now steal them back and add to them, by way of interest. I am yours to command, Don Miguel."

Miguel handed him a twenty-dollar gold piece. "Not one word of this to anyone, Senor Diablo. You must return to the Domec ranch just as though nothing had happened. Remain there—when I need you, you will get word. Tell the Domecs your ankle got caught in the kink of a riata and it will be all right. Adios for the present."

And with smiles and protestations of love and fidelity, the youthful caballero took his leave and departed.ငာ

Endnotes

1. A compadre is a child's godfather. The term "compadres" refers to the father's relationship to his child's godfather—it also is a Spanish colloquial expression for pals. *(LaRousse Spanish Dictionary)*

2. Miguel did not marry in this country, but he is known to have fathered at least two children, Marcelina (1860-1880) by Espiritu and Natalia (1877-1956) by Librada Arustica (Mascarel's stepdaughter, from the previous marriage of his wife Jesus Feliz). Librada later married Nathaniel Pryor Jr.

9

The Folds Multiply
A Runaway Bull—Etchemendy's Safe
Goyeneche Sells Some Sheep

For months following the incident with Manuel Dominguez, peace reigned at the Escorpion. Everything was serene, not so much as a summer cloud or zephyr disturbed the placidity of the beautiful sea overspreading the space between Leonis and the Domecs.

On the Domec ranch, Manuel had received many expressions of sympathy concerning the injuries he had suffered. A few cynics thought it marvelously strange, however, that such an expert with a riata as Manual should become entangled in a rope's kinks and be dragged by the leg like a captured coyote. To these critics, Manuel merely smiled and said: "Accidents will happen—even to the greatest of men."

The grass had been young and green when Manuel made the transfer of lambs. Now all was sere and yellow, and the grain harvested. One day Domec, in a very humble and dejected state of mind, appeared at Leonis' house, hat in hand. He was received politely by Miguel, who inquired: "What good wind has blown you here?"

"All of our sheep have disappeared as though the earth had swallowed them," Domec answered dolefully. "We have scoured the country, searched the canyons, and traversed the mountain ridges. But our sheep are gone."

"How many have you lost?"!

"About one hundred and twenty."

"So this is the good wind that carries you to the Escorpion," said Leonis. "What can I do for you?"

"I thought perhaps our herd may have got mixed with yours—and that you would permit me to examine them and see."

"Most certainly."

Away went Domec after the herds he could see scattered about the plain. After a time he returned to Leonis with the information that he had found his sheep. Some of them were marked, and there could be no mistake about it.

"My good brother-in-law," Leonis said. "I will go with you and see for myself." The two set forth, like Damon and Pythias, until they reached the first herd, where Domec pointed out several sheep he identified as his.

"No," Leonis said, "these are mine."

"But see the marks on the ears—that is not your brand, that is not your ear mark. It is the ear mark of Jeronimo Lopez, from whom we bought the original stock."

"I bought ewes from Jeronimo Lopez myself," answered Leonis, "and I claim that the sheep we are looking at are the ones I purchased. Do you recognise any of the lambs?"

"Not in particular, but my herd has disappeared. Since I find the mothers here, I assume their lambs followed them."

"How many sheep did you purchase from Jeronimo Lopez?" inquired Miguel.

"Twenty-five head."

"And when was that?"

"The first of last January."

"And they were all ewes."

"Yes, all ewes."

"Each ewe has since had a lamb?"

"Yes."

"All the lambs lived?"

"Every one."

"Then," Miguel responded in triumph, "you ought to have fifty sheep in your herd—not one hundred and twenty!"

"Yes, that is true," Domec said, "but I also bought some lambs."

"I know," answered Leonis. "You bought lambs from Dominguez at twenty cents a head. Is that not true? . . . And of course you knew that Manuel had stolen them from me. I am suggesting, Senor Domec, that Manuel—having stolen most of your herd from me—has now stolen them away from you and sold them to some other person. What do you think of that proposition?"

Domec became evasive.

"Senor Domec," Leonis continued, "let me speak plainly. Manuel Dominguez was caught in the act of stealing my lambs. He was taken to Los Angeles, where he made a full confession and I have his statement in writing—signed and sworn by him. I am not offering to show it to you, and this is the only information I will give you concerning it. If you think I have any of your sheep, the best thing you can do for me—and the worst thing you can do for you—is to sue me for them. Then you will have an opportunity to read, or hear read and explained to all, the confession by Dominguez. We are neighbors, Domec, we are not brothers-in-law. In the past you have called me by this familiar term, but I reject it. If Marcelina is your wife, then I want you to understand that Espiritu only works for me as a servant. Since we are neighbors, I have tried to be fair with you. You have been otherwise with me."

"Now then," Miguel said to the silenced Domec. "Suppose we consider ourselves even and take a new start. I will do right by you from now on, but every time you or any of yours attempt to deal crooked with me you will surely be tripped. Let us drop this episode, Senor Domec— you have no sheep on this ranch. There are no stray sheep belonging to you among my herds. Au revoir, Senor Domec. The next time you go into the sheep business, go slow."

Domec returned home to find Dominguez. Not seeing him at the house, he asked Marcelina after him. She replied that she had not seen Manuel all during the day and it was already noon. The fact is, Manuel had left to help search for the missing sheep. He was over on the south side of the mountain ridge, having transferred his allegiance from Domec to Leonis. When his whereabouts was discovered, the Domecs understood the situation. Dominguez had betrayed them—sold them out—and now they were worse off than ever.

"You had better stick to your lime burning, Senor Domec," Marcelina told her husband. "Trying to run opposition to El Basco Grande in the raising of horses, cattle and sheep is away higher up and above your capacity. You are a good lime burner. Better stick to your trade."

A few days later, a large number of sheep disappeared from the Encino, where some Basque men were renting pasture from Vicente de la Osa, the ranch proprietor. Some of these sheep were afterward discovered in Leonis' herds—and the same proceeding and resolution ensued as had taken place between Leonis and Domec. The missing sheep always remained at the Escorpion, however, and thus it happened that Leonis recovered not only all his lost lambs, with all their step-mothers, but also perhaps many other sheep that had never belonged to him. He stood by them and, as a result of the first incident with Manuel Dominguez, steadily increased the size of his herds.

Another year or two rolled around, and Don Miguel had become an established power in the land. His wisdom and judgment were renowned. The Mexicans thought he was a wizard, while the Basques thought he outwitted them in every transaction they shared. His herds increased with such remarkable rapidity as to astonish his competitors in the business. The man never seemed to sleep—he would remain in Los Angeles all day, transacting business and contriving plans for the future, be seen at supper, and then the next morning at daylight he would be out at the Escorpion, rousing his men to get out to work. It was work, work, work. Still, the workers liked Don Miguel. He was just, he was generous, he paid well—and he was always willing to lend a helping hand to a poor devil in distress.

One day an event occurred in Los Angeles that made Miguel popular among the Americans. He happened to be in town when a herd of cattle was being driven through the streets, as was customary during that period. Suddenly, a maddened steer escaped from the herd and dashed furiously down Main Street. The beast crossed the plaza and went on to Commercial Street, spreading terror along the way. Just south of Commercial, several ladies approached—one of them wearing a red dress—and the frenzied steer dashed toward it. From positions of safety in doorways and windows, the townspeople cried their horror. As for the ladies on the street, they ran to the nearest sidewalk, but there seemed no possibility of escape from the maddened animal. He charged toward them—his tail erect, head down, and gleaming sharp horns lowered for the intended victim.

At this most critical instance, an unarmed man stepped directly in front of the steer, caught it by its horns—which he then deftly twisted—and threw the animal flat on its back. There it lay, with legs extended and eyes set, quivering in the agonies of death. The mighty Hercules, Miguel Leonis, had wrenched the beast so mightily he broke its neck.

Miguel was lavishly praised, thanked, and congratulated. It was nothing he had not done before, he told his admirers, "Not everyone is strong enough to do it, of course, but—if you have the coolness and the strength—a simple twist makes wringing the neck of even the biggest bull as simple as snapping the neck of a turkey or goose."

Soon afterward, around the middle 1860s, Leonis became embroiled in a very bitter lawsuit with a Basque named Etchemendy.[1] Somehow or other, Etchemendy had subsidized someone at the Escorpion ranch in order to possess a bundle of papers that belonged to Leonis—papers of most important character. Having acquired these valuable papers, Etchemendy had no scruples about boasting of the fact, telling all that he had the papers safely locked away in his room safe in Nigger Alley.[2]

Leonis decided to reclaim his property. So, on a Sunday evening when the populace was enjoying the performances of the maromeros,[3] Miguel boldly entered Etchemendy's room and had just picked up the safe when he was surprised by the arrival of Etchemendy and some of his friends. Miguel escaped through the door, with the heavy safe on his shoulder. Once outside, he ran across a back lot, pitched the safe over a wall seven feet high, and sprang over it. Finding the metal box had burst open from the fall—revealing his package of papers—Miguel secured them, then picked up the safe and pitched it into a great water canal. He got away safely, with his papers, and the next day it took seven men to get the safe out of the water and return it to its place in Etchemendy's room. The story brought Miguel great admiration from the Basque population and, together with the incident of the steer as recounted by the Americans, made him a local hero.

Leonis grew richer and richer. Although there were some most enterprising and industrious Basques engaged in the same line of business in Los Angeles county, they could not begin to keep pace with him. The increase of his horned cattle was a marvel, by careful breeding and wise selection, his horses had become the best in the country and his sheep multiplied at a rate that was beyond precedent.

Among Miguel's many rivals, leaving out Etchemendy, were Gaston Oxarart, Pierre Larronde, Domingo Amestoy,[4] the Garnier brothers,[5] and Goyeneche. All except Goyeneche become immensely wealthy through their care and enterprise in the sheep-raising business.

Goyeneche kept his sheep at the San Francisquito, later known as Newhall ranch, and, as it happened, one day Manuel Dominguez was sent on an errand to the Laguna de Chico Lopez[6] and the Yano Verde. On his way back, he stopped with Goyeneche's sheep herders in the San Francisquito. While there, Manuel's eagle eye noticed a number of Leonis' sheep mixed in with those of Goyeneche. On his return to the Escorpion, Manuel reported what he had witnessed, but he could not estimate with any certainty the number of sheep he had seen. To his best judgment they numbered in the hundreds. Now it should be remembered that Leonis'

Domingo Amestoy   *Pierre Larronde*

sheep numbered in the many thousands by this time. A few hundred less would hardly make a perceptible diminution, unless they disappeared out of one particular herd all at once.

Miguel gave Dominguez full instructions and provided him with a sufficient amount of coin to go over to Goyeneche's ranch—pretending to be on a hunting excursion—and deal liberally with the sheep herders. He was to furnish them with wine, cigars and such things that relieve the monotony of sheep herding. After trying to judge, so far as possible, the actual number of Leonis' sheep in Goyeneche's herds, Manuel was to find out how they happened to be there.

For his secret expedition, Manuel took a mule laden with good things to eat, drink and smoke. Once arrived, he sought a shady grove near the Goyeneche corrals and pitched his camp. Of course the sheep herders called upon him. Sheep herders pine for company, and Manuel knew how to be sociable. He informed them of his supposed business in their neighborhood, opened his demi-john of wine and dealt out the cigars and tobacco—making himself a most liberal host.

The sheep herders did not know that Manuel was employed at the Escorpion, and they freely confided in him all they knew. They talked about their patron, when they characterized as very stingy. They complained that he stinted them in the way of provisions—they had to buy their own wine and managed to get along only in a half-starved condition.

The question came up of the sheep—how many Goyeneche had and; the number he started with. Finally, Manuel carelessly suggested that Goyeneche must have purchased a small herd from Leonis. The herders answered that quite a number of sheep came from the Leonis herds, but that they had been acquired from someone else—10, 15 or 20 sheep at a time, until there were about 300 in all. Most of the sheep were ewes that had borne lambs since they came to Goyeneche.

Manuel tried to learn the name of the person who had brought the sheep, but the herders could not tell him. They knew only that the sellers were two Mexicans. One they called Don Valentine and the other they said was Don Juan. As to where these men lived or what their business was, Manuel could gain no information—but he inferred who they might be. Don Juan was a new novice rancher at the Laguna de Chico Lopez, and Manuel thought he also knew where to find Don Valentine.

Having elicited all this information, Dominguez broke camp and traveled to the Laguna de Chico Lopez, where he camped with Don Juan. Don Juan was a half-breed Indian, the illegitimate offspring of a Spaniard father, and an enterprising fellow he was—with a great amount of self-assurance and bravado.

Manuel made himself agreeable with Don Juan—he carried with him a fresh supply of aguardiente from the cellars of Andres Pico—and encouraged the rancher to become immensely confidential with him. Manuel even offered to sell him a few sheep, telling him he had the sheep hidden in a canyon. He confided in Don Juan that he had stolen the sheep from Leonis, that he was running quite a trade in this line of business but had no fear of discovery because Leonis had the utmost confidence in his honesty.

"I have about fifty head of these sheep now," Manuel told him, "but I don't know where to find a purchaser. That is my main trouble."

"What price do you want for them?" inquired Don Juan.

Sheep were then worth from two to three dollars per head, and Manuel indicated he was willing to sacrifice his small herd for a dollar each. He offered to divvy with Don Juan if he could find him a purchaser—he would give him two bits a head.

It was only then that Don Juan informed him that he had a purchaser for the animals, but that the price for a good class of sheep would be only six bits a head. If Manuel were willing to sell each sheep for seventy-five cents, it would be an easy matter. Don Juan went on to explain that he had run quite a trade with Goyeneche, who purchased the several lifts he had made out of Leonis' herds. Since Manuel was a sub-majordomo for Leonis, Don Juan proposed that between the two of them a profitable side trade might be possible.

As for the fifty head of sheep waiting in the canyon, Manuel readily agreed to sell them to Goyeneche. "Except," he asked, "where is he?"

"Oh," said Don Juan, "he lives in Los Angeles, you know. But when I notify him that I have sheep to deliver, he will put the money in his pocket and come out to the ranch to pay for them on the spot. All I have to do is gallop into Los Angeles and appoint a day when the sheep will be delivered. Goyeneche will be on the grounds in person to pay the money, cash down. After I arrange the particulars with Goyeneche, you and I can meet at San Fernando. We can pick up your fifty head and drive them over to the San Francisquito."

All very nice. The arrangements were made, and Manuel packed up and started for San Fernando, with Don Juan riding alongside. After a point, Don Juan continued alone into Los Angeles to see Goyeneche. Manuel remained at San Fernando to await his return.

On the following day, Don Juan returned to San Fernando and reported his mission had been sucessful. Goyeneche would be at the ranch to receive the sheep at daybreak, in an arranged place, at which time he would pay for them.

"Now," said Don Juan, "all that remains is to get the sheep into a position so we can drive them down to the place appointed. We must be there exactly on time."

Leaving Don Juan at San Fernando, Manuel went over to the Escorpion to report to Leonis the success of his secret mission—telling him where the stolen sheep would be delivered and that Goyeneche would be there. The same night, fifty head of sheep were selected, separated from the others, and driven to a canyon that enters the San Fernando plain very near to the Santa Susana Pass. Well before dawn, Manuel galloped the few miles over to San Fernando and soon returned in company with Don Juan.

They leisurely drove the little herd from the canyon, over the ridges and down the slopes, until they got them to the edge of the San Francisquito valley within a short distance of the trysting place with Goyeneche. There they rested and slept, alternately guarding the little herd. Before daybreak, they were on the move to the appointed place and arrived in good time.

As soon as it was light, Goyeneche approached, coming from the direction of his sheep corrals. After friendly greetings and respects duly paid to Manuel's canteen of aguardiente, the business of the meeting was discussed. The sheep were duly counted, the coin was handed over, and Goyeneche started with the little herd toward his corrals. He had progressed but a short distance, passing a clump of live oaks at a little recess on the side of the canyon, when he was surprised to feel a heavy hand grasp the back of his neck.

Leonis was upon him and, notwithstanding that Goyeneche was a burly Basque who weighed about two hundred pounds, Leonis raised him from the ground with a clutch on the back of the neck and shook him—as a terrier shakes a rat. Gasping for breath, Goyeneche begged to be released, and released he was—with an immense crash upon the ground that took his breath away. A few well-placed kicks brought him back to his feet, however, and Leonis held him fast by the collar as he turned to see what had taken place with the other two, the dons Juan and Manuel.

Upon the appearance of Leonis, both caballeros had bolted for their mustangs, which were tied to bushes nearby. But Don Juan was confronted by the sight of Dreux holding a double-barreled shotgun, while young Fabricio de la Osa covered Manuel with a carbine. The game was up for all concerned.

In the conference that ensued, Manuel gave the whole thing away as to how he had conspired with Don Juan and Senor Goyeneche to steal sheep from Leonis, and how great numbers had previously been stolen that could now be found in Goyeneche's herds.

"What have you to say about this, Senor Goyeneche?"

"I purchased the sheep honestly. That is all I have to say."

"We will see about that," responded Leonis, as he proceeded to tie up Goyeneche. "I will take you and these two gentlemen to Los Angeles, where I will turn you over to the sheriff. I will prosecute you—for stealing my sheep—and I think we have abundant proof to send all of you to the island for a healthy period of your lives. Now let us proceed to San Fernando. You can all walk. Dreux, you and Fabricio will lead the two horses, and I will lead Senor Goyeneche." He mounted his horse, the end of the rope fastened to Goyeneche in his hand.

Then Goyeneche spoke up dolorously: "Don Miguel, let's have a talk about this thing. I am disposed to do what is right."

"Let us see what you will do," said Leonis.

"You can search my herds, and you can take every sheep that ever did belong to you."

"I see—and I suppose we might agree on round numbers. Count them out, Senor Goyeneche, and you can give me a bill of sale for them. You know that I am a buyer of sheep."

"I think I have about a hundred and fifty of what were your sheep, although they are mine now because I paid for them."

"I think you have a full thousand, Senor Goyeneche," said Leonis. "So, if you will have your herds driven to the corrals and count me out a thousand full-grown sheep, I will not take the trouble of searching your herds. But, as I said before, I will take your bill of sale for the lot."

After much haggling and two or three false starts on the part of Leonis toward San Fernando, Goyeneche consented to his terms.

"Now, we must have an understanding," said Leonis. "Not one word to your herders, when the sheep are being delivered, that this is anything other than a fair transaction. You are selling the sheep and receiving a price. I further agree not to molest Don Juan or Don Manuel. You can all go free."

The two caballeros brought their persuasions to bear upon Goyeneche, and he again agreed. They all proceeded to the corrals and cabins, where the sheep were driven up and one thousand counted out. A bill of sale was given and duly witnessed. Then, with protestations on the part of Leonis of future amity toward Goyeneche and with like responses on his part and much compliment, the two separated with a wish expressed on both sides for an opportunity to meet at Los Angeles, so they could celebrate the transaction over a good dinner at the Layayette Hotel.

The thousand sheep were driven away, and in the evening they were safely corraled at the Escorpion. Is it a wonder that Leonis' herds multiplied? ∾

Endnotes

1. In *Amerikanuak*, Jean Etchemendy is described as a French Basque born in 1830 who migrated first to South America, where he was living as late as 1847. Coming to California, he joined the gold mining camps, where he experienced moderate success. In 1851 he established a bakery in Los Angeles, and shortly thereafter he went into the sheep business. Etchemendy died in 1872. (pp. 347, 425).

2. About Nigger Alley. Before the Americans came to Los Angeles, the street was known as Calle de los Negros, a reference to the dark olive complexions of the family whose home was located off this alley. Americans translated the street name literally, and prejudice soon made it a racial epithet. In fact, it was not blacks who populated Nigger Alley but the poor of Mexican descent and the city's Chinese inhabitants. For years this was the site of Los Angeles' underworld, its red-light district. (See W.W. Robinson, 1959, pp. 50, 54-55) In *Fortune Favors The Brave,* Bell describes the exact location of Nigger Alley: It was at the north end of Los Angeles Street, where the wide road narrowed to about 40 feet across. The end of the alley opened into the Plaza, which at that time was a large irregular square, bare of trees and grass and cut across with crooked paths. (pp. 34-35)

3. Maromas were rope dances, according to Horace Bell (1881/1927, p. 9). *The Larousse Spanish Dictionary* describes maromeros as tightrope walkers.

4. In *Amerikanuak,* the names of Gaston Oxarart, Pierre Larronde and Domingo Amestoy appear on a published list of Basque persons who in 1850-1851 applied for passports from Buenos Aires and listed California as their destination. (pp. 414-415) Oxarart and Larronde reportedly once worked as sheepmen in the Cahuenga valley. (p. 227, citing Loyer and Beaudreau's *Le Guide Francais,* 1932) Amestoy in particular was able to parlay his modest beginnings into a fortune—his sheep operation became one of the largest in southern California during the 1860s. In 1871 he purchased half a million dollars worth of shares in the new Farmers and Merchants Bank of Los Angeles. (p. 227)

5. The Garnier brothers were two Frenchmen who acquired Rancho El Encino from Vicente de la Osa. A two-story stone building they constructed near the old adobe house still stands near the spring.

6. According to *In Pursuit of Vanished Days* by Marion Parks, the Laguna de Chico Lopez—now known as Elizabeth Lake—was along the stageline road from Fort Tejon. It was the property of Francisco Lopez, nephew of the Don Francisco Lopez who discovered gold in Placerita Canyon. When Lopez came into hard times, he lost the property to his mortgage holder, Miguel Leonis. In later years the region was re-named Leona Valley. (p.201-202)

IO

Odon Reveals a Secret
El Escorpion Passes to Miguel

don's interest and steadfast devotion to Leonis became more marked as time went on. The old Indian became increasingly alarmed and concerned over the difficulties accumulating about Miguel. He feared greatly that his beloved friend might be assassinated, or that a mob of his enemies might appear in the night, set fire to his buildings, and kill him when he appeared in the light, perhaps even destroy his most faithful servants. Of course, in the judgment of Leonis himself, no danger of the sort was thinkable. Odon had grown to be very old. He had passed the age of eighty and perhaps was somewhat childish.

One night he invited Leonis to his house and, after scouting the premises carefully, he shut the door and opened conversation by saying, "Patron, I fear greatly that some calamity is going befall you, and necessarily upon all of us. Indians from the Mission have told me rumors of evil portent. Your enemies lurk in every hiding place and I no longer know what to expect. I have seen suspicious persons scouting around at early dawn and late in the evening. Strange men have come to the house and made inquiries that I could not understand because they spoke in riddles. But, from all I could gather, an attack is to be made upon us. The barn will first be set on fire and, as we come out of our house and run toward the barn, we will be shot from ambush."

"I have a great secret to impart to you," he continued. "We will be able to use it as necessary, either for the security of our persons or the concealment of our valuables. There is a great cave, patron. It is nearby and I am the only living person who knows of it. For years, its very existence has been kept a profound secret—one that has come down from father to son in my family. Many years ago, when my father was about to die and he felt the chill hand of time upon him, he took me to this cave. It is a wonderful cave, patron. The old Indians called it the 'Cavern of the Dead'—because for generations our dead leaders have been interred in it. It is a very large, patron, you could build a small town inside of it. I want to show this to you. The secret of its existence will die with me, for I have no son to whom I can impart the knowledge.[1] Our line has died out. I am the last of it. Yet you have been more than a son to me—my benefactor, my protector, you have been everything to me. The sands of my life are fast passing away. I only hope I can live to see you through your troubles, but I don't know. I may be called upon to join my fathers at any day, or at any hour of the night. Patron, I want you to know about this great cave."

Leonis was curious, of course, and he put many questions to Odon concerning the cavern, but the only answer he could get was, "I will show it to you tomorrow. I cannot describe it to you. It is too great, it is too grand. Sometimes I think it is the Other World. I would like to be buried there, because it is the home of my ancestors. After this, patron, after I have shown you the cave, I desire to make you a deed to the Escorpion. You have amply compensated me for it.[2] You have supported me as though I were a great man. I have had good clothes to wear, which you have furnished me, a good house to live in, a warm clean bed and plenty to eat and the wine jug, patron, has never been empty. All I ask is that I may end my days with you in the peace and plenty, contentment and protection that I have had at your hands. Tomorrow, patron. Tomorrow we will see the Cavern of the Dead."[3]

The next day, after the morning's work had been done and the dispositions of the day made, Leonis buckled on his revolvers, shoul-

Photograph by Ray Phillips.

Entrance to the "Cavern of the Dead." Called in those days "La cueva de Munits," after the sorcer who was believed to live in the cave, according to Indian mythology, this cave is in a canyon just southwest of El Escorpion. Today it is on the Ahmanson Ranch, just west of Valley Circle Boulevard, on land which may become a park. While not as large as the cave Bell describes, its location fits the story. (Thanks to Bob Edberg for the information used in the above description.

dered his rifle, handed a canteen to Odon and threw one across his own shoulder, and the pair started for the mountain. They crossed the arroyo

Photograph by Ray Phillips.

Inside the "Cavern of the Dead."

a little above the sulphur wells and ascended the mountain in a southeasterly direction. After climbing and zig-zagging and winding around past great rocks and crawling through numerous crevices, they came to a very narrow, sharp and rocky ravine. The rocks came together in the form of a wedge and rose to great heights, sometimes over-arching and lapping so as to shut out the light of day.

Finally Odon halted. He sat down and, after they drank from their canteens, he remarked, "There, patron, there is the cavern." Miguel looked all about but could see nothing.

"You will," replied Odon. He raised to his feet, advanced a short distance and came to the end of what seemed a passageway. Miguel followed, and when they turned a sharp angle of a jutting crag, they found themselves plunged in darkness. There was an opening there but the darkness was so intense nothing could be seen within a few feet of them. Miguel gazed in silent astonishment.

From a package he carried, Odon produced two tallow candles, lit them and gave one to Miguel.

"You must stoop down," he said, "or you will knock your head against the rocks."

Bending over, Miguel pressed forward after him. Within five minutes of winding through the dark, Miguel noticed that the passage had widened and increased in height. Here Odon halted and seated himself upon a rock, inviting Miguel to do likewise.

"We will rest here for a few minutes," he said. "We have got through the outer passageway, and now the cave will grow larger, wider and higher as we progress. Soon we will soon be in the heart of the mountain."

"Is it all darkness for all of it?"

"Just wait and you will see," said Odon. He again started forward, with Miguel close behind him.

Five minutes more revealed a wonderful sight. The feeble light from their two small candles reflected back from thousands of stalactites that hung suspended from a vast dome—effectively lighting up the cavern as though innumerable fires were burning. Odon took the two candles and cemented them to the rocks with their dripping tallow. The Indian then lit two fresh candles from his package, handed one to Miguel, and continued on deeper into the cavern.

Miguel kept close company because he was awestruck, for the first time in his life a sense of fear overcame him. He felt himself tremble.

Observing this, Odon remarked, "There is no danger. We will soon be at 'the tombs of the dead.'"

By this time the cavern seemed so immense as to be limitless. The floor was level, except for the stalagmites that for untold ages reared their heads in an everlasting attempt to meet their fellows from above. So brilliant were these stalagmites from the reflection of the candles that they illumined the passage as though it were some great lighted dining room or place of human habitation.

"Odon," Miguel asked as the frightening thought occurred to him, "suppose our candles go out or burn down, how in world are we to get out?"

"Don't be concerned," Odon replied, "I have provided for that." He showed Miguel a ball of strong twine. One end had been tied to a rock at the entrance of the cave and Odon had been reeling the ball off as he moved forward. "Even if our candles burn out, I have brought enough to last us for several nights if necessary."

They made further progress to the interior, and soon came upon a vast level floor covered with a labyrinth of mausoleums. Miguel took note that the vaults appeared to have been excavated from the rocky floors of the cave, with blocks of granite covering them.

"Here are the tombs of our dead," Odon said quietly. "The Indians who formerly inhabited this country were not the same people as today. For many, many years there have been no burials here. Our people ceased to work; they became degenerate. They could not excavate a tomb; they could not fabricate the granite rock block to cover one if they did. But, see, patron, here are so many tombs covering the remains of the people who dwelt here, many hundreds of years before the Mission fathers came to this country. I think, if we were to get into a war—if the Mexicans should come back here from Mexico to destroy and turn out the gringos—we can bring our valuables to this place and stay here in quiet and security."

The cavern was immense. More remarkable than that was the fact that it was ventilated. From the surrounding walls opened other smaller caverns, angling in from all directions, through which came currents of air that made the atmosphere smell fresh and sweet—free of the confined musty odor of ordinary caves.

Strangest of all, at the most northern extremity of the great cavern, they could see a beautiful placid lake of clear, cool, refreshing water. It was large—in width, about thirty or forty feet. Its length could not be determined because it extended underground out of sight and also because of some large crags that came to the water's edge.

"This is the fountainhead of the waters that form the Los Angeles River," said Odon. "It is one of God's water tanks. The water that rises and flows down the Escorpion arroyo to the creek comes from this tank, through some small springs we see in the foothills. They are only smaller leaks from this great reservoir. Subterranean channels and seepages pass underground and first burst forth at the Encino. It is true, patron, this is the source of the Rio Porciuncula of Los Angeles."

"What about the sulphur water at the Escorpion and at the Encino, Odon? Where does that come from?"

"Quien sabe?" answered the old Indian. "Perhaps there is another reservoir in some of the branches of this great cave that are still hidden from us—and may remain hidden for all time. But think how nice it would be to live here, patron, if we had sufficient provisions and fuel with which to cook our meals. Perhaps we will be compelled to use this cavern in this way at some future time. But for now I am satisfied that I have shown it to you—you have witnessed the wonders of the Cavern of the Dead."

"I had been so afraid," the old Indian continued, "but now that we are here I feel at peace. If there is trouble at the Escorpion, we can store our valuables here. We can bring provisions, barley and wheat. The cavern is large enough that we could even bring in our herds, if pressed. Then, when the troubles are over we can come out, having saved ourselves and as much else as possible. You may have heard, patron, that the Mexicans intend to retake this country. That is what Joaquin Murrieta[4] tried to do years ago. Joaquin used to come to the Escorpion with his followers, and it seems he had information from some quarter that there was a great cave here in which to hide in case of emergency. But no one knew of it but myself, and I did not like Joaquin so I told him nothing. He was a great man-killer. He killed gringos and robbed the Indians, as well as his own countrymen. I was glad when the gringos finally killed him and destroyed his best men. The others went back to Mexico."

Miguel tried to calm Odon, assuring him there was little danger of Mexicans invading this country. Although he saw no use in the cavern for such a contingency, he was wonderfully glad to have seen it—and pleased that Odon wanted to show it to him. The thought even occurred in his mind, unexpressed, that someday antiquarians and scholars might find these relics of a lost people more interesting and more wonderful than excavations in other prehistoric places.

After viewing the revelations for a long time, finding themselves hungry, the two ate some food they had brought and drank their water and wine. They had been gone for hours and thought it about time to leave. When finally they emerged from the entrance, the darkness of night was upon them and they found it very difficult to descend the mountain to the canyon. When they reached, the ranch house it was near on to midnight.

The next day Leonis went to Los Angeles and had his lawyer prepare a deed for the land that Odon was about to convey to him. The lawyer, not knowing that the Escorpion was a valid Mexican grant to Odon and his brother Manuel from many years before—conceiving it to be only an Indian holding—wrote out the formal parts of the deed and left a long blank space in which Leonis could insert the description, such as he and Odon saw sufficient to describe the Escorpion.

When he returned to the ranch, Miguel explained the deed to Odon and suggested that he direct him on how to fill out the descriptive part of the document. This Odon readily agreed to do, and they went to the Picacho, a rock butte rising almost perpendicular from the edge of the mountain range to a great height, a few hundred yards south from the ranch house.

Having seated themselves at this high point, Odon said, "We will start here, and with our eyes we will cover the plain of the Encino. Now you take your pen, patron, dip it in ink and draw a line this way, commencing right here now" and he directed a line to be drawn southeasterly for about a mile. Then he directed Miguel to draw another line in a northeasterly direction, and then another southeasterly and northeasterly and southerly, with the last line running directly east until it struck the Encino. This made the description of Escorpion's boundary's look like a large worm fence, running from a given point and diminishing in zigzag angles until it all ran off to a point.

This curious description for many years afterward became a source of litigation in the courts—because, while the proponents of the deed contended that it covered the entire Escorpion range, its opponents were able to point out that there was no connection between the initial point and the point of termination. The lines did not come back to the place of beginning. And so it was held by the courts, the deed was void for want of description.

Endnotes

1. According to federal census records (1850 and 1880), Odon had a son named Bernabel.

2. Odon was in no position to pass full title of El Escorpion to anyone— at the time he owned only a fractional ($^2/_{12}$) share in it himself. The original land grant (1845) deeded the property to three Indians, Odon, Urbano and Manuel. Manuel was Urbano's 15-year-old son. Odon and Urbano became brothers-in-law when Urbano married Odon's daughter Marcelina. Originally, each Indian had a $^1/_3$ interest in El Escorpion. Marcelina stood to acquire more, because she could inherit from both her father and her husband. (Notwithstanding Bell's story,

it was not Marcelina who married Pierre Domec but her sister Maria Dolores.)

Joaquin Romero, a Mexican, became a part owner in 1849 when Odon, Urbano and Manuel each conveyed part of their interest to him. This mean Romero owned $5/12$—almost half—of El Escorpion. Manuel retained $3/12$ interest, and Odon and Urbano each kept a $2/12$ share.

In 1861 Joaquin Romero sold his $5/12$ interest to Miguel Leonis for the sum of $100. In Chester Cohen's monograph *El Escorpion,* a description is given of the deed information: The property was said to have two sections. One was Old Escorpion, described as the site of Urbano's house (approximately Roscoe at Valley Circle Boulevard), which presumably included the old Indian village (at the entrance to Bell Canyon). The other was New Escorpion, "where Pedro Domec and other persons known as Indians live." (p. 17, citing Los Angeles County Recorder Book of Deeds 5, pp. 312-413) The information on the deed is a good example of the hazy and inaccurate property descriptions that plagued El Escorpion records. In fact, Domec's house was on ex-Mission San Fernando property—for all practical purposes, he was a squatter. (p.21)

By 1861, Miguel Leonis already owned almost half of El Escorpion and was trying to buy all remaining shares. The Indian Manuel died in 1861, leaving no heirs except his father Urbano. When Urbano died in 1864, Marcelina inherited Urbano's and Manuel's shares combined—a $5/12$ interest. Determined not to sell to Leonis, Marcelina gave her power of attorney to a neighbor, Antonio de la Osa, who in turn passed her ownership to another sheep rancher, a Civil War general named Edward Bouton. Later Marcelina sued de la Osa for defrauding her, but: the court ruled against her—confirming the deed held by General and Mrs. Bouton. After settlement of the suit, Mrs. Bouton approached Leonis with another suit, to physically divide El Escorpion in proportion to their interest—Bouton's $5/12$ to

Leonis' $^7/_{12}$ (by then he had acquired Odon's $^2/_{12}$). To avoid a partition, Leonis purchased Bouton's interest for $800.

So, Odon did indeed convey his interest to Miguel—for $1.00 "and other valuable considerations." His interest, however, amounted to $^2/_{12}$ ownership. In later years it was said that Leonis had cheated Espiritu out of her rightful inheritance of El Escorpion. Considering the number of children Odon had who could inherit from him, any interest Espiritu might have received was miniscule.

3. In a canyon just southwest of El Escorpion; indeed, in the time of the story it would have been considered a part of El Escorpion, is the cave in the illustration. In Indian mythology it was called "La cueva de Munits," after the sorcerer who was believed to live in it. Today the cave is on the Ahmanson Ranch, just west of Valley Circle Boulevard (altough there is no access) on land which may become a park. Around 1905 Horace Bell lived for several months at El Escorpion—in one of the adobe houses at the site of the old indian village. This is when his son Charley, for whom Bell Canyon is named, owned the property. Horace was certainly familiar with the area landmarks, and may well have interviewed local people for background for the story. The local Indians had a legend that a tunnel connects Castle Peak (the high point called the Piacho in this story) to another mountain. The tunnel supposedly runs from north to south.

The actual cave is much smaller than the one Bell describes and, needless to say, contains no lake and no tombs. There are no other known caves in the area. (The above information comes from Bob Edberg and Gerre Hoppe.)

4. Joaquin Murietta was a notorious Mexican-born bandit from Los Angeles, the subject of an intense manhunt throughout California during the early 1850's. He was captured and killed in 1853, on the border of the Tulare Valley.

Leonis

II

The Great Wool Speculation—Miguel Plans a Trip Home—A Bear Enters the Corral

It was May, 1869, and there had been nine successive years of copious rains and great grass crops. Stock of all kinds had multiplied, and prosperity reigned throughout the sheep regions of California—especially so in the southern counties, Los Angeles in particular. Wool was low in price and had been so for some time. In 1869 the price was down to eight cents a pound, twelve and a half cents was considered a high price.

One day Leonis came to town and, as was his custom, he called at Mascarel's. That evening after dinner, Mascarel produced a voluminous letter he had received from his brother, the merchant in Marseilles. Skipping over the fraternal and social news, Mascarel came to a pause and said, "Now Miguel, I want to read you a business proposition of great importance. My brother has somehow or other got into some diplomatic and state secrets that, put together, he says make the prospect of war inevitable between France and Germany. He tells me he is reshaping his business affairs to meet the coming crisis, for such a war will shake the commercial relations of the world. And the particular stress of his letter is this—how I can make money from this crisis by judicious investments here . . ."

Leonis interrupted, "I don't see how war between France and Germany can affect investments in Los Angeles county. We are so far away, we may as well be on the moon."

"Just listen," Mascarel said, "and you will see the point. My brother, who is a very shrewd merchant, tells me the prospect of war between those two countries will cause a great advance in the price of wool. He advises me to invest in wool—every dollar I can get. This is a secret between us, Miguel—for me and for you—because my brother specifically mentions your name and suggests I offer you the same advice he is giving me. We must invest every dollar we can get into wool. Mind you, if the Jews find out about this, we will not be able to make a dollar. So, keep it to yourself. Wool is now down to eight cents. How much money can you invest, Miguel?"

"I have about thirteen thousand dollars in the bank."

"And I have some money of yours in my hands," Mascarel said.

"You have? Well, I didn't know it."

"Don't you remember? In May of 1857 you left with me seventeen hundred dollars. You gave an order to Menendez for one thousand, which I paid, and I lent out the remaining seven hundred dollars at interest. I kept a strict account. There were seven hundred dollars left in my hands."

"But, wait," answered Miguel, "I have been getting provisions from you for years, and all manner of trade. I supposed you took the money out of my seven hundred dollars, along with what I paid you as I went along. I did not think there was much, if any, left of that money."

"Well, let me show you the statement. I prepared it with great care, knowing you were coming to town and could see it. I want you to know exactly where you stand financially, so we can go to work and buy all the wool we can get hold of in this county. I have lent out your money on pawns, good notes, and short-term mortgages—gaining from two percent per month compound interest to as high as five percent per month, a conservative rate of interest for this county but I kept your money going all the time. It has never rested, Miguel, there has never been an idle dollar. Look at the statement—I have seven thousand dollars for you."

"Sacre bleu," said Leonis. "Was there ever such a man? And such honesty! Why, you could have kept every cent of this and I would not have thought less of you for it. I realize that in the ways in financial investment I am profoundly ignorant. Indeed you have been more than a brother to me, Josef. Now, tell me what to do about this wool business."

"You have twenty thousand dollars and I will put in another twenty thousand. I will work the Jews for whatever wool they have to sell me. You work the Basques and, between us, let us buy all the wool we can get."

On the next day Mascarel bought a thousand bags of wool at eight cents a pound. By the time it was found out that Mascarel was buying up wool, he had purchased about every bag in the city, latterly paying as high as ten cents a pound. Meanwhile, Miguel scoured the ranches and did likewise. He made contracts and advanced money on the next shearing. All forty thousand dollars was invested in wool, and Mascarel was able to dig up another twenty thousand to invest in the spring clipping of 1870. Once all this was accomplished, the two speculators rested.

They had acquired some 40,000 pounds of wool, with half as much more coming in on the next spring shearing. When clipping commenced in the spring of '70, there came a shock that made the earth tremble as in the throes of an earthquake. The two mighty war powers of Europe were about to come together in mortal combat. The commercial world was set agog, and financial speculation became the order of the day. When the price of wool started to go up, lo! The Jews of Los Angeles discovered that wily Mascarel and Leonis had absolutely circumvented them, the two were holding all the wool in the county. Immediately, the price of wool went up—and kept climbing until it reached $1.25 a pound in Los Angeles. Then Mascarel said to Leonis, "Sell! Sell! Don't wait another day."

So they sold. They sold every pound of their wool at the highest notch on the market. The price never got to be a cent higher, and in three months it was down to sixteen cents a pound. The war between France and Germany turned out to be very sharp and decisive. Speculators had predicted a long and continued pounding, with a resultant long and continued interruption in commercial transactions—but they were disappointed. The clouds cleared away, commercial matters resumed their routine, and speculators who had purchased wool at a dollar and a quarter a pound found themselves financially ruined. Mascarel and Leonis, however, had realized a profit of nearly a million dollars.[1]

"And now," said Leonis to Mascarel, "I would very much like for us to take a trip together to Europe."

"What on earth for," said Mascarel.

"I have some unfinished business at Cambo. That, and I would like to see someone again—a woman. If you must know, her name is Marie Grazieuse Etcheverrigaray.[2] You've been like a brother to me, Josef, and I would like you to meet her."

Mascarel swore a mighty oath in English—one he had learned on the Savannah frigate when he was a California volunteer in the service of the United States, back in 1846 and '47.

"Did you understand what I said, Miguel Leonis?"

"I don't speak English."

"The Spanish language and the French language put together are insufficient to express my abhorrence, my consternation, at hearing that you want to go back to some old Basque sweetheart of yours! She must be old and ugly by now, Miguel. Promise me you will not speak that name again in my presence. I had to call on the aid of the English language, such as sailors use at sea, to express how I feel about this infliction you put upon me! Oh, very well, then. But if we must speak of her, let's just call her Marie. So, why haven't you given her up. Miguel?"

"Why should I? I loved that girl and I once promised I would come back for her. She's not too old—over thirty now, it is true, oh, but she is still beautiful."

"Halt, Miguel. Don't you go any further."

"No, I will say this. Marie is the most beautiful woman in all the Pyrenees, if I tell it myself. I have a photograph of her, taken a year ago at Bayonne, that I have never shown you. Here, look at it. Tell me if she is not still beautiful."

"Por amor de Dios," said Mascarel, examining the likeness. "She does look like a queen. Well, I can't blame you for wanting to go back for her. You go to Cambo and get her—and bring her here to Los Angeles and set the people wild. Show them what the Pyrenees can produce. But, Miguel, be careful about going to Cambo. You must remember those Spanish revenue officers. Besides, you can't go, Miguel, I can't get along without you. And I am afraid that if you go to the Pyreness you might not return."

"That is where you are mistaken, my good friend. I will come back. And there will be no trouble, because I fixed that more than a year ago. Good old Father Jean at the monastery arranged it for me. Ten thousand dollars was what was required—when I sent that amount to the high dignitaries of Spain, they condoned the offense. I am now able to travel freely to Bayonne and Cambo and Bilbao, or any place I desire, and to return. It is all fixed and paid for, and I am ready to pack and leave."

Miguel asked Mascarel to figure out a settlement between them and to convert all of his share into European exchange, so that he might take the money with him.

"But what are you going to do with so much money?"

Then it was that Miguel revealed to his friend his great ambition, that he was a member of the Lion's Brood and how, years before, he had committed himself to raise this money for the cause of Basque independence. His intent was to take this money to Father Jean and then return to California to work at accumulating more. Eventually he would go back and help set up a separate government in the Pyrenees, until at last the Basque people could live in a country run by Basques.

"I can raise an army of a hundred thousand men," he said, "and with this money we can arm them. All Basques will support us, and in

Isais W. Hellman. A prominent Los Angeles banker, he loaned money to Leonis on occasion, and was a co-executor of his estate.

our mountain fastnesses we will not only divide, we could whip all Europe. Father Jean is secretly working upon the leaven of revolution—I am raising the sinews of war. This is very important to me, Josef. Help me. How much do you suppose I can carry with me when I go to the Pyrenees?"

"That depends on how much you want to leave behind."

"I want to leave twenty thousand dollars with the banker Hellman, and no more. Please excuse me, my good friend. There are certain reasons I want to leave that amount of money with Hellman, and you needn't know why. I will make you a factor of my business during my absence, however, so that all monies coming from my affairs will be in your care. But I need twenty thousand dollars to be in Hellman's hands."

"That is fine. Isaiah Hellman is an honest Jew—he helped us make this large amount of money on wool, you know. He advanced us the money we wanted over and above our own money. But we have paid him back, neither of us owes a dollar. So, to answer your question. You will be able to carry with you European exchange in the value of three hundred and fifty thousand dollars."

The friends parted, and Miguel returned to the Escorpion.

An incident not uncommon on California ranches occurred on the Escorpion shortly after Leonis' return from Los Angeles. Near the residence and at the rear of the great barn was a corral for the keeping of cows with very young calves. At about midnight a great lowing and bellowing was heard from among the cattle in the corral. The dogs were barking furiously and there was a great uproar in full blast. All hands rushed out the doors, Leonis ran for the corral and found Manuel Dominguez already there.

"Oso! patron! Valgame Dios! The bear is killing all the cows!"

Miguel sprang over the fence into the corral. In the light of the moon, he could see a massive bear that had thrown a cow to the ground and now had his huge jaws clamped on the cow's neck. With lightning speed, Leonis seized the bear from behind—by the ears—and bodily heaved it from the cow before the astonished bear had time to realize what was happening. Bears do realize, a bear is very smart—smarter than some human beings. The bear arose on his hind legs, Leonis still holding him fast, and there they both stood upright as the bear attempted to face about and confront his tormentor.

To avoid this happening, Leonis shoved the bear forward, jamming him into a corner angle of the corral and holding him there. The corral was strong, and the contest between the great man and the great brute was terrific. The bear tried to turn about and face the man, while the man used his prodigious strength to keep the bear pinned in the corner.

Leonis called out to Manuel, and the young man entered the corral with an axe in hand. "No, no," Miguel said, "If you try to strike him with the axe you might hit me. Take your knife and stab him."

"I have no knife!" said Manuel.

"Then take my knife. It is attached to my belt, and hurry! I am getting tired."

Dominguez, about as cool as Leonis himself, drew the knife from its sheath and thrust it deep into the bear's side, just behind the shoulders. This only seemed to lend strength and fury to the animal, for he lurched about and succeeded in throwing Leonis to the ground. Whereupon Manuel gave him another thrust, resulting in still another roll and another tumble—with Leonis still trying to hold the bear in order that Manuel might dispatch him.

By this time the dogs had joined the fracas and some of the Indians appeared on the scene. One Indian rushed up with an old United States musket to which a bayonet was attached. On the first opportunity, he thrust it through the bear's neck, but still the fight went on. Sometimes Leonis would be on top of the bear and sometimes the bear was on top of Leonis. Finally, an Indian came with an axe, the one dropped by Manuel. He watched for an opportunity, then struck the bear across the back of the neck, just under the crown of the skull. The axe penetrated with sufficient depth to cut the spine, and the bear rolled limply over, in the agonies of death.

The concern was for Leonis as he pulled himself to his feet, still cool as a gladiator.

"Are you hurt?" they inquired.

"Very little, very little. I was able to keep his teeth away from me. There are some scratches on my body and my legs, but I don't think they amount to much."

Leonis was wearing a thick pair of overalls made of the strongest kind of cottonade and a jumper of the same cloth character. His wounds really were only superficial, and in a day or two he was as well as ever.

This was considered one of the best bear fights—between man and beast—that had ever occurred in this part of the country. Later it was ascertained, upon dissection of the bear, that the first thrust of Manuel's knife had penetrated a vital organ, and it would have been only a matter of time before the bear died. The other thrusts were less mortal, but the brave Indian with the axe had finished the fight.

Leonis was much lionized on account of his exploit with the bull in Los Angeles and the bear at the Escorpion. In response to compliments, he insisted on giving the honor of the fight to the Indian and to Manuel—each of whom he presented with a purse of two hundred dollars.

Not long after the fight with the bear and preparatory to taking his departure for Europe, Leonis gave a grand fiesta at the Escorpion. The great bare floor was smoothed down for dancing. Tables were arranged in the willow grove, and pits were dug for the purpose of roasting carcasses of beef, sheep, pigs and fowl. The whole countryside was invited to attend, and they came from as far away as Santa Barbara and farther than Los Angeles.

Don Andres Pico was made the guest of honor and Colonel Andres Larios y Pacheco was the grandiloquent master of ceremonies, while Domiguez was a man of all work. He assisted everywhere and was master of the roasting pits. The Domecs were there, also the Goyeneches, the Garniers, the Etchemendys, and all of the people who had suffered unpleasant relations with Leonis in the past. This was because on such gatherings, the patron—the man giving the feast—was supposed in the polite ethics of the society to be forgiven by his enemies. He in effect extended his right hand to them. If they attended the feast, they came as friends, leaving all enmity behind them. It was the making up of past differences and forgiveness of all offenses, and after an enemy attends a fiesta given by a former enemy, that was supposed to be the end of it, and henceforth they were to be friends.⁓

Endnotes

1. The complete truth of this story is questionable. However, in Spalding's *History and Reminiscences; Los Angeles City and County*, a remarkably similar event is described: "In the preceding year (1871) the price of wool steadily advanced and in this year culminated in a speculative boom. Mr. Newmark says that his firm made advance contracts in November, 1871, while the wool was still on the sheep's back, and continued buying everything that was offered until April, 1872. Their first shipment to San Francisco brought forty-five cents per pound. The going price in former years had been from ten to twelve cents per pound. The boom collapsed shortly afterward, and Mr. Newmark

writes it down as the most disastrous wool season in our history." (p. 203)

2. This name appears in Miguel's will, but there is no indication that she was other than a family relation—a daughter of Miguel's sister Marie. Grazieuse was a resident of Algiers when her uncle died in 1889.

12

Miguel's Return to Cambo, Marie Gracieuse

"Here is a draft on the Bank of France for two million francs," Mascarel told Leonis, handing him the papers. "That is the equivalent of four hundred thousand dollars. Your share of the wool speculation does not amount to quite that much, but I made up the balance for you and we can settle some other time. Also, here is another draft on the same bank for the same amount, which I wish you to hand over to my brother at Marseilles. Perhaps, should the exigency arise, Miguel, I will permit you to use that money. I fully appreciate and sympathize with you in this great undertaking you propose. I have often thought of the situation— that a Pyrenean republic could and should stand as impregnable as Switzerland, and that its people ought to be as free and as progressive. The Basques are a distinct people—with no relation to any of the other races dominating Europe. They should be independent."

Mascarel continued, "But my assisting you is contingent upon one thing—on the Basque people setting up a republic. Ah! I am a republican in the fullest meaning of the word! You yourself must know the value of republicanism from your fifteen years' residence in this grand and free country. You are not a prince by descent, Miguel—you are simply the offspring of a great leader, a historic general who commanded the armies of a great republic. And you will make yourself a great leader, no doubt. You have all of the elements, Miguel. Impress this upon the mind of your adviser and mentor. If he wants the sympathies of the world and especially of this great country, first he must declare for a republic!"

Miguel scanned the drafts of the large amounts of money, and Mascarel assured him that they were all right—if nothing else, because they had been procured for him by Hellman.

"If I were master of an empire, I would trust Hellman as my financial minister," Mascarel remarked. "He is a great financier, honest as well as sagacious. So, how long will you be gone, Miguel?"

"Not more than six months. The time consumed in traveling alone will take about two months, and I may not care to remain over two months in the Pyrenees—so you can count on me being back at any time between four and six months."

"Return as soon as you can, Miguel. I will keep a good eye on your business, and especially on Manuel Dominguez. I tell you, that fellow is no good. He is loyal to you only because he fears you and because you pay him well, but he is a dangerous customer, my friend. But rest assured I will do the best I can for you during your absence. Well, the stage leaves from the Bella Union Hotel in a few minutes. Let me walk with you there."

Several weeks later, Miguel Leonis arrived at the gate of the old Carthagenian stronghold, the monastery at Cambo. A gray-haired Father Jean was writing in his study—when a young porter appeared at the door to inform him a stranger at the gate demanded asylum.

"Send him in," said Father Jean.

The boy returned in the company of a very imposing-looking man whom he had been instructed to identify as "Leonis, of California." Father Jean at once stood up and rushed to receive the visitor with open arms. He was overjoyed to see him and, after the usual salutations and inquiries and responses were made, observed his guest carefully. In the fifteen years since he had sent the young fugitive out of the monastery so mysteriously, a great change had been made in Leonis. Time and contact with the world had made such improvements in his appearance that Father Jean was at once surprised and gratified.

Turning to the boy, Father Jean said, "Call in Jean Pierre, my secretary." "Is that the same Jean Pierre of old?" inquired Miguel.

"The same," answered the Father. "He is still a little wayward and sometimes unreliable—I may even say rascally—but, even so, I trained this fellow and he is a most excellent secretary. As a matter of fact, he is the most expert man with a pen that I have ever known. He is a full grown man now, you will see."

A few minutes later, the secretary bowed himself into the father superior's presence.

"This, Don Miguel," said Father Jean, "is the boy who brought you into the monastery, that day fifteen years ago when you were a fugitive. Look, he is more changed than you are."

Miguel took a careful look at the secretary. Jean Pierre had grown to be quite bulky, and he walked with a wallowing gait. His shoulders were large and his limbs well developed, except he was still excessively knock-kneed and his feet turned out, very much like those of a turkey. Although only about thirty years of age, he was already partially baldheaded. In one respect there was little change—that old cunning leer was still upon his face. He seemed unable to look Miguel straight in the eyes. Jean Pierre's gaze invariably glanced off as if he searched for something in the distance, and then he would look at the floor. When he spoke, his unconvincing smile made Miguel uncomfortable. Miguel realized he still did not like Jean Pierre a bit, and he felt embarrassed by his presence.

Observing this, Father Jean pointed to a pile of loose manuscripts and told the secretary, "Here, take this writing of mine, carefully transcribe and punctuate the writing and then you may bring it back to me for signatures."

With a very profound bow, Jean Pierre took the manuscripts, kissed the hand of his father superior, and bowed himself out of the room—leaving the door slightly ajar.

Father Jean did not notice the door. "Now we are alone," he said. "What news do you bring me, Miguel?"

"Better than news, I bring you some money. Here is a draft on the Bank of France, made payable to me," Picking up a pen, he said, "I will endorse it to you, Father," and he handed the draft to Father Jean.

Father Jean looked at it and then at Miguel. Then he looked at the draft again. He read it carefully. He examined Miguel's endorsement. Then he leaned back in his chair: "Two million francs? A draft of two million francs on the Bank of France? Can I believe my eyes? Is this real? That you have made this money and have placed it at my disposal?"

"Yes, Father, it is a part of five million I left here to work for—for you, for myself, for our countrymen, and our common cause! I left an equivalent draft with the merchant Mascarel at Marseilles that, upon a contingent necessity, I may be authorized to use. If so, that brings us to the full sum that I undertook to earn. I will have taken care of my end, Father. Now, tell me, what do you say are our prospects, the outlook?"

In a brief conversation, Father Jean informed Miguel that the leaven for a revolution had been started and was fermenting—that some of the strongest men of the country had agreed to join when called upon. They were sowing the seeds among the more humble classes and discussing among themselves the proposed uprising.

"But I don't want you to make yourself known in it at all, Miguel. You must leave this all to me. These proposed leaders drop in here at times and we discuss ways and means, lay plans and then they go forth and perform their allotted duties. The change in public feeling throughout the Pyrenees, on both sides of the line, has been almost as radical as the change in your financial condition. Money has been promised—yes, and money has been paid in. I have here in my strongbox fifty thousand francs as a nest egg for the revolution fund. But Miguel, it is time for the evening meal," and Father Jean rang his bell.

Jean Pierre, who had been eavesdropping at the door, tiptoed out of hearing and disappeared. When the young boy came, Father Jean ordered supper to be set in his private dining room.

"Oh, by the way, have you seen Mademoiselle Marie yet?" Father Jean asked carelessly.

"I have not," answered Miguel, flushing. "I came directly here from the main coach, speaking to no one. And I noticed that no one seemed to recognise me. I assume that you, and those present in this monastery, are the only ones who know of my presence in the Pyrenees? Although it doesn't matter, since the trouble with the Spanish Customs officials has been fixed. I think I will go out—and make myself sociable. Do you know where I could find Marie?"

"I will send for her immediately!" Father Jean smiled. "She can come here and have dinner with us." The boy accordingly was instructed to call one of the monks, young Father Joseph, who was ordered to go into the village and summon Marie Etcheverregaray. Supper was delayed for an hour, until her arrival, and meanwhile Father Jean and Miguel resumed their conversation, discussing affairs in the Pyrenees and the out-look for the Basque people in California.

"How are they getting on in that country, Miguel? Are they mak-ing money as fast as you?"

"Oh! no, not by any manner of means—but some are doing very well. You know Gaston Oxarart, Pierre Larronde, Dominto Amestoy, and there are others I could mention who also are becoming very rich. The money I brought you, however, was realized through good advice from your friend Pierre Mascarel of Marseilles to his brother Josef, my business partner in California. We realized eight hundred thousand dollars out of the French and German war."

"You made so much money out of that war? What had you to do a war in Europe? What can sheep in California have to do with it?"

Miguel was only too happy to explain the great wool speculation and its happy financial termination. "But I got all the rich Basques down on me because they say I beat them. If buying their wool at a fair price is beating them, then I must plead guilty. I had the knowledge and the money and the wisdom to buy—wisdom acquired from Pierre Mascarel of Marseilles, I admit. So, I bought the wool from the Basques, for which I paid them with good money, and they are angry with me. I made enemies of every one of them, which I regret—but I am gratified that I was able to bring you the drafts and to put them in your hand myself."

At that moment, the imperious beauty Mademoiselle Marie entered the room. In Father Jean's presence, the former lovers' meeting was cordial and dignified. Miguel and Marie shyly exchanged warm and heartfelt congratulations, and gave each other compliments on each one's improved appearance.

The three adjourned to the dining room, where the conversation took another turn., "Marie has been partially let in on our secret operations," Father Jean explained. "She is a most discreet woman, the only one I know with whom I would venture to discuss this subject. She tells me what the women of this country are thinking—she goes among them, taking and also giving out her opinions and ideas as to our right to an independent government—and she reports that the women are ripe for revolution. They are willing to work for it, many even say they will fight. Marie tells me she has been to Bayonne, and that it is boiling over with patriotic fervor."

"It's true," Marie interjected earnestly. "Women in that city, from the highest ladies to the poorest servants, are partisan and patriotic to the core."

A general conversation ensued on the financial question and on how long Miguel expected to remain in the country. Marie in particular wanted to know about California and of what had happened to persons she knew who emigrated there.

All of this was overheard by Jean Pierre, who eavesdropped from behind a door. He had a certain place in the dining room where he could conceal himself without fear of detection. And so it was that the three conspirators' secrets became no longer secret. Unwittingly they had taken the friar Jean Pierre into their confidence.

When supper was over, the father superior had Father Joseph conduct Marie to her home. He and Miguel talked longer for some time longer and then retired, with Miguel remaining the night as a guest of the monastery.

13

Friar Jean Pierre Makes His Move
Miguel Leaves France

A fter Father Jean and his guests had retired, Friar Jean Pierre emerged from his place of concealment and hurriedly left the dining room. Once in his own room he threw himself upon his cot and, as was in his character, began to talk to himself, "Well, well, well. This time I have surely possessed myself of secrets I may be able to turn to good account. So Father Jean has built up a nest-egg for a revolutionary event, and the principal men of the Pyrenees are sowing the seeds of revolution. Perhaps Miguel Leonis himself plans to be the revolutionary leader. My master, Father Jean, could be minister of state. Even Gracieuse, Pleader of the women. Why, we may truly have a Pyrenean republic!"

"I don't doubt Spain and France might relish some information concerning this uprising—so I think I can turn this to my own advantage. I will need to go about it slowly, however. I will watch the game. This Miguel is a big fellow and I remember him as a daredevil. I am afraid of him. But there are ways to dispose of Leonis! I could give the information to the police—no, that might not be wise just yet. However, let the leaven work. You can be sure Jean Pierre will be here, keeping his eyes open. When I think of all that money! Fifty thousand francs—Oh! My fingers itch to handle it! My eyes burn to see, just to gaze upon it! I want it. I must have it!"

"For the present, however, I will content myself with making plans to convert that treasure to my own custody. Of course, Father Jean considers it perfectly safe. No one suspects us poor friars of having, or wanting, any great store of money. Even if they did, it probably is as safe here as in the Bank of France, or in the bottom of the sea. What I need is to find a way to get to that box. I can carry the money into the open country and hide it somewhere, until such time as I may use it for my own benefit. Very probably, Father Jean would not miss it for months, he seldom goes to his strongbox and I don't imagine he has much else in it. But wait! He has Leonis' two million franc draft. That, he is apt to keep in the strongbox until he can have the money placed at his disposal in the bank. How he will arrange to do it I don't know, but I am certain he will store the draft in his strongbox for the present. All I need to do is watch him. I know his hours of sleep and those shall be my hours of sleep. I shall shadow him every hour that he is awake, until at last he goes to the strongbox and I can find out what he does with the key. I may be able to get the draft as well. If I do, I will just skip the country—perhaps I'll go to Mexico. I know some people in Mexico. Jose Esteinou is a banker in the capital of that country. And then there is Etchegaray and the Larronde brothers in the city of Leon. Those men have became great and rich in Mexico. All I need to do is get there, even with only fifty thousand francs and no more, and I will be well on my way to financial grandeur.

"As for Leonis' bank draft, surely there is a way. I know, I can hurry to Paris, have the draft cashed, and continue on my passage to Mexico. Ah! Father Jean, you have trained me too well. And you say I am the best secretary and the most expert penman you know. You don't know the full extent of my skill. I can write your letters and sign them myself, and no one can tell the difference. Why, yes, a power of attorney from you might be useful. Those three co-conspirators think they are so smart—they think they are great people. But I guess Jean Pierre can best all three put together. I will outwit them all."

Jean Pierre had an affinity for wine and all this scheming and planning had the effect of making him thirsty. He left the room to slip through the corridors and into Father Jean's dining room, where he lifted a quart-sized jar of wine from the table and returned with silent footsteps to his dormitory cell.

Seating himself, he took a long drink, and began muttering aloud again, "They say wine sharpens one's wits. Good, because I need to think a little further on this matter. Miguel Leonis says he intends to remain here a month or two. I can observe them until he leaves, and in the meantime I must also find a way to get Father Jean's key to the strongbox. As I see it, the only problem is Miguel. I can't help it but I dread him. When I am in his presence I almost feel him clutching my throat. The very thought of it chokes me." Jean Pierre took another strong pull at the earthen wine jar. When the vino Catalan was finished, Friar Jean Pierre wallowed over to his cot and fell on it in a drunken slumber.

Very early the next morning, before Father Jean had resumed the routine of his daily duties and while Miguel was still aleep, Marie was at the monastery gate requesting to see both Miguel and the father superior. Miguel was sent for and, seeing the two as he entered Father Jean's study, expressed his surprise to find Marie at the monastery so early in the day.

"I left yesterday evening feeling very disturbed and I was unable to sleep all night," she told them. "I reproach myself for not making known my suspicions last night, but now, after mature reflection, I am taking the earliest opportunity to speak with you."

"What is it?" asked Father Jean and Miguel in the same breath.

"While we were at supper, discussing those critical questions of state, it was my solemn conviction that someone was concealed in the dining room closet. I seemed to be able to hear his breathing, even detected his efforts to suppress it. I could sense his hand attempting to hold down the throbbings of his heart."

"Well, well, well," answered Father Jean. "Let us go into the dining room and examine that closet."

The three went into the room and Miguel opened the closet door. It was empty, but on the floor the first thing that met their gaze was a rosary.

Father Jean picked it up and said, "Yes, it appears that perhaps someone was here last night, and I would say it was Jean Pierre. I know this to be his rosary. He would have had no excusable reason to enter that closet, so it could only have been for the purpose of eavesdropping upon us—and I would guess that in his agitation the rosary broke, as you see, and slipped to the floor. Well, at least now we know, and we all will have to keep an eye on Jean Pierre. Although I always knew his capacity to be a rascal, I never suspected such treachery."

Leonis spoke up, "I would like to wring his neck and throw him over a high wall. If he so much as attempts to cross my path, I will do it."

"Father, this Jean Pierre is a snake in the grass!" exclaimed Marie. "He is full of mischief, malice and treachery. I have known him to be this way since his youth. I detest him and now I also fear him. He makes mischief in the village and, Father Jean, do you know that he goes away from here to the pot-houses, where he drinks like a Spanish soldier?"

"But he goes out only when I send him on errands or for the transaction of some business. He has always seemed straight enough in matters I trusted him with. What proof do you have of this drunken behavior, Marie?"

"Proof? Why I have seen him myself, as drunk and helpless as a pig in the mire! I am friends with Madam Ballade, and on one occasion I was visiting the family at Ballades Canteen—she and I were about to leave the house—when what do you think? In the middle of the hall whom should we meet but Mr. Ballade with two servants, dragging and carrying this Friar Jean Pierre from the top room, where he had fallen helplessly drunk, to a place where he might sleep himself sober. Mr. Ballade told us to remain until they disposed of the friar and then im- plored us not to speak of it. He admonished the two servants, under pen- alty, to keep silent on the subject, and said that he had cleared the the tap room of visitors before the friar began to show signs of inebriation. Jean Pierre was kept at the tavern all night, until he was sufficiently sober to enter the monastery before you missed him. This was my own observa- tion—my own sight! I also have heard it whispered around the village that he is out at night, he leaves the monastery clandestinely and is up to all manner of licentiousness. A keeper of bad company, he is, none of which has been known to you, Father Jean. But a bad egg is this Jean Pierre. I am so glad you have found him out!"

With the discussion ended, Marie left the monastery. Later in the day Leonis also left, and went into town to make himself known, visit relatives, and meet old-time friends.

For the next two or three weeks, nothing occurred to disturb the quiet of the monastery. Father Jean went about his daily routine of devotional business, and he continued to employ Friar Jean Pierre in the writing and transcribing, dressing up of documents, writing of orders, and doing of all the clerical work pertaining to the Father's many duties in the business of running the monastery. Thus it was that Jean Pierre was able to constantly observe Father Jean, watching for an opportunity to find the keys. One day he saw Father Jean go to the strongbox. What the father superior put in and what he took out, Jean Pierre could not tell, but he noticed that the key to the strongbox was carried not at Father Jean's girdle but attached to a large bunch of keys, which the father superior kept in a small purse hidden in the inner pocket of his surplice.

"So far, so good," thought Jean Pierre. "Now, the next time I find my master sound asleep I will search his pockets. If I find the key I will go directly for the fifty thousand francs. I wonder what form it is in. If it is in gold or silver it will be much too heavy. I hope it is in paper money—that would be so much better."

Jean Pierre did not realize that Father Jean and Miguel had planned for just such a contingency. After observing the friar's movements, they had concluded he was indeed after the fifty thousand francs, so they devised a plan of their own to accommodate him. Five sealed packages were prepared—each labeled "French Bank Bills, 10,000 francs" but containing only worthless paper—which then were placed in Father Jean's empty strongbox. Father Jean and Miguel surmised that Jean Pierre would not risk opening the packages while in the monastery. As to the revolutionary nest-egg money, Father Jean concealed it elsewhere.

One evening soon after the father superior had been seen at the strongbox by Jean Pierre, the rascally friar was reported missing from the monastery. How he had gone out, no one knew. No one was allowed to pass the portals without special permission of the father superior, either in writing or by his special messenger. Nevertheless, Jean Pierre was gone.

Once Father Jean and Miguel were satisfied that the friar was actually absent—no longer within the monastery walls—they made no disturbance about it. None of the other friars was given to understand there was anything amiss, or that anyone had mysteriously disappeared from the place. Accordingly, Father Jean and Miguel were not surprised when they went to the strongbox and found the five packages missing, though the key was still in its place. Jean Pierre was absent and their suspicions were proved true. But they had circumvented him, for he had carried away only the bogus packages.

"There is danger in the air," Miguel remarked. "A special danger to me. If Jean Pierre discovers that he has been duped, he may not return to the monastery at all. He may sell whatever information he has to the authorities and leave the country or conceal himself."

"I fully agree with you," said Father Jean. "The air is full of evil portent. If he returns to the monastery I will take care of him. However, if he does not return, then you, Miguel, must immediately leave the Pyrenees. You must get out of the country quickly and return to California as soon as you can."

The next morning, however, Jean Pierre was back at his post of duty—smirking and smiling and looking profoundly complacent, as if nothing unusual had occurred. How he got out and how he returned so mysteriously was a riddle. Father Jean was careful that his manner toward his secretary be unchanged from what it had been. He remained good-natured, dignified, kind, and indulgent.

Shortly before noon, Marie came to the monastery to see Father Jean. Miguel's presence was requested and, when the three were closed in a room together and the surroundings carefully examined to guard against the eavesdropping friar, Marie stated her business, "Last night I know for a fact that Jean Pierre was out again all night. I know because from the time I first saw him in the town I shadowed him—and I was out all night! I was dressed in disguise, so he never suspected."

"Let me tell you where he went!" she continued. "It was all very curious. He visited various places and then he went to the cemetery. What he did there I can only surmise, but I think he concealed something. Then he visited the police, and this alarmed me for I was afraid for Miguel. Although it seems very improbable that the information he conveyed to the authorities would be used so soon, it is my opinion that Miguel is in imminent danger. For some reason or other, Jean Pierre despises you, Miguel. I don't know that he would implicate me or Father Jean, but you I am sure he would give away. Do you not agree, Father Jean?"

The father superior reluctantly agreed, "I am in full accord with your views, Marie. It is therefore also my judgment that Miguel should not delay his departure."

Miguel asked for leave to speak with Marie alone, and as soon as Father Jean stepped out of the room, Miguel laid open the feelings of his heart. Before he would leave the country again, he said, he wished for them to marry—and for her to accompany him to California.

She positively refused—that is, she told him that she loved him, and wanted to marry him some day, but that this was not the time. She was engaged in the important work of the revolution, she had committed herself to be part of the program, and she was needed here and could not abandon her cause to go to a foreign land.

"Father Jean tells you I have made myself useful among the women," Marie said. "The truth of it is, I also am useful among the men. Being a woman, I have a woman's license. I can speak freely here and am not considered a suspect. Any Basque man who would speak as I have will find himself shut up in a prison."

"When you return, Miguel," she told him with earnest conviction, "and the war cry is raised, then and only then will I become your wife—to share with you the toils and dangers of this revolution, and to rejoice with you when it is accomplished! Until then, you have your work and I have mine. Go about it, my love. Do what you must do. I will do the same."

So it was that Miguel left the Pyrenees alone. It was arranged that he would leave the monastery and depart from the town in darkness that same day. Marie arranged for a private conveyance to take him to a neighboring station where he could, unobserved, take the main coach for the nearest point on the railroad. He would ride through to Paris, then to Le Havre, where he could board a ship to New York.

As a further precaution, Father Jean decided that though the simmering of the revolution would be kept warm, there should be no agitation. Those engaged in its propaganda were admonished to go more slowly.

As for Miguel's plans, he fully intended to return to Los Angeles and make further financial arrangements to acquire the use of the draft Josef Mascarel had sent to his brother at Marseilles. Whatever other money Miguel could raise—from disposal of his great herds of sheep and cattle and of all his landed interests in California—he would bring back to purchase the revolutionists' arms and munitions of war.

The next day Miguel Leonis was not observed in the streets of Cambo, nor was he seen to enter or emerge from the gates of the monastery. Even Friar Jean Pierre took occasion to comment on that point, "Why is Don Miguel absent from the monastery? He had been here for weeks and now suddenly he is gone!"

Father Jean offered no information on the subject, and as time passed it became generally conceded that the great Leonis had indeed departed as mysteriously as he had arrived. He had disappeared under circumstances as sudden and as secret as when he left the Pyrenees fifteen years before. Many marveled at this, others expressed disappointment. The few knowing ones rejoiced.

It was much later that the agents of the French Police made inquiries as to the whereabouts of the gigantic Leonis, only to be told he was long gone—he had returned to California.

Several months after the sudden disappearance of Leonis, a great clamor was raised in the monastery—such an uproar as had never been heard within the walls before. The friars were on a rampage, alarming Father Jean, as the usual placidity of the place became transformed into the unintelligible fury of a mob. Surging through the corridors, a crowd of friars dragged and kicked another friar as they made their way to the audience hall. Father Jean had been summoned, and when he entered the room he was astonished to see that it was Friar Jean Pierre who was the subject of all this indignity. The wrath of the monastery was being vented upon him, and it was only when he was dragged in front of Father Jean that the clamor ceased and the friars stood around in respectful attitude. Yet Father Jean could see their breaths still came short and fast and their eyes flashed with anger. The muscles of their faces quivered, their hands were clenched. "What under the name of all the saints can be the matter," Father Jean began.

Friar Jean Pierre was roughly thrust forward, as old Father Michel stepped up to state their case, "This recreant friar, Jean Pierre, has been discovered in the commission of a horrible crime," the old monk said, "a crime so disgusting, so venal, so unnatural . . . that my tongue is paralyzed and I cannot speak it. Ah! Let him be flayed alive!"[1]

The bruised and bleeding wretch to whom he referred stood in sullen silence.

Father Jean addressed himself to the assembled friars, "Now let us go quietly about this business. Let me hear proof. I want also to hear what the accused has to say and then I will pass judgment upon it."

Father Michel called Friar Lazarus forward as a witness to tell the story—which cannot be written here, but it caused the assembled friars to hide their faces in the capes of their gowns, and even good Father Jean turned his face away in shame, though he remained master of the situation.

Upon being satisfied as to the truth of the charge, he ordered that the miserable culprit be taken to the penance room and given the lash. He was to be put on a diet of bread and water, and be lashed morning and evening, for a period of nine days. Then his head was to be shaved and his monastic robes burned. He would be given the clothing of a scullion and cast out of the monastery.

As to Jean Pierre's youthful accomplice in this unnatural crime in which they were discovered, we will cover him with the mantle of charity.☙

Endnotes

1. Years later, in decrying Goytino's unsavory character, a Los Angeles editor of *Le Gaulois,* a french-language publication, alluded to Goytino's having been forced to leave a French monastery because of "a series of crimes against nature." The quote was cited in an article titled "The French Press in California," which appeared in the *California Historical Society Quarterly.* (The full quote appears in this book on page 200).

14

Jean Pierre Expelled—Enlists Aid From Ballade

Pitiable indeed was the condition of the disgraced friar when he was kicked out of the monastery. To make matters still worse for him, the night air was cold and chill, and it was raining. He left, barefoot and bare-headed, wearing scant apparel that had been cast off by one of the kitchen scullions. His body was sore and raw from the scourging he had received, and from his bread-and-water diet he was so weakened he could scarcely stand upon his feet. Even so, Jean Pierre had great physical strength, and he braced himself up bravely as he wended his way to the tavern belonging to Ballade.

He knocked at the door. The house was closed, its windows darkened, for the guests of the tap room had departed and the lodgers and the family were retired for the night. Fortunately, Ballade himself appeared to answer the knocking at the door, and was surprised to recognize his midnight visitor.

"For the love of your patron saint, help me," Jean Pierre cried as he fell into the room. "Give me food and shelter—I am so famished. I am sore. I am dying. But don't ask me for explanations until my weakened spirit is recovered. First of all, my good friend, give me some wine—or aguardiente would do better."

Ballade lighted a candle and the two entered the tap room, where a great goblet of wine was poured out and swallowed by the forlorn ex-friar, all at one breath, He was conducted to a small room on the ground floor, where Ballade brought him something to eat. Ballade also provided some dry garments and assisted Jean Pierre in removing his shabby and dripping clothing, preparatory to putting on the clean clothes.

When he saw his guest's back, he was horrified and demanded to know the meaning of it, "What has happened to you, Jean Pierre? For the love you bear your dead mother, tell me!"

"Please forbear, my good friend Ballade. I do not want to have to think about this damnable affair for at least one night and a day. I have had enough of it. I prefer to forget it. Give me some more wine."

"Put on these clothes first and you will feel better. But I think that I had better put some oil on your back first. I have never seen the like in my life! Wait a minute before you put on these clothes," and Ballade departed from the room.

He returned shortly with a bottle of sweet oil that he poured upon Jean Pierre's wounds, gently rubbing it in. Then the clean dry clothing was put on and the patient reclined upon the sheets.

Ballade offered more wine and more food, but warned, "You must eat sparingly, my friend, and do not gorge yourself on wine. You seem to have been fasting as well as having been scourged. What have you had to eat for the last few days?"

"Musty bread and foul water from a ditch, and for nine days and nights I was castigated before breakfast and after supper. Only bread and water twice a day—oh, but I want to forget it, I told you, so let it rest for the present. I will drink this wine and perhaps I can sleep." Jean Pierre drained another tumbler full of red wine, then rolled over on his bed and fell into a profound slumber. Carefully covering his guest's body, Ballade retired to his bedroom and went to sleep.

The next morning at a late hour he looked into the room but found Jean Pierre still wrapped in deep slumber, which continued until mid-day, when Ballade served him with a dinner. A big bowl of mutton broth was first on the menu. Jean Pierre wanted only the wine, however, which was administered to him sparingly.

"Mutton broth is what you want and what you need," Ballade told him. "The wine you will have to do without until you get stronger."

"Does anyone know I am here?"

"None other than myself," replied Ballade, "and none other shall—until it is your wish to be known. I see there is some deep mystery here, and I propose to keep all others in the dark until I get a full explanation. Who shaved your head? What the devil does it mean anyway?"

"Let me rest for a few days and then I will tell you all about it. Keep me concealed. All I need is some food and wine until I recover my strength of body and equilibrium of mind. Then I will tell you, Ballade. Now I come to remember, however, that you must still have a large package of papers that belong to me. You remember I once left them with you for safekeeping? Are they all right?"

"Oh! yes, they are all right. Certainly. I have taken good care of them, and when they are needed you shall have them." At that Ballade departed the room, leaving the ex-friar alone in his misery.

It required more than a fortnight before Jean Pierre felt he was himself again. Hair had begun to sprout again upon his shaven cranium, the dry skin had partially peeled off from his well-tanned hide, and his appetite had modified. Yet no one other than Ballade knew of his presence in the house.

One day Jean Pierre asked for his package of papers, and upon receiving them he spent a long period in a minute examination of their contents. Then he said to Ballade, "I need for you to get me a respectable suit of clothes."

"Where is the money?" exclaimed his put-upon host. "I have been thinking seriously as to how and when I am to be compensated for all of this care and maintenance I have given you. I may keep a tavern for the money there is in the business, but do you expect me to buy clothes for you?"

"I know where to go to get money," said Jean Pierre, "but I can't go dressed the way I am. I must have the suit."

"If you have money, can you not give me an order for it?"

"No, this is something I have to do in person. I have the money concealed, Ballade—fifty thousand francs! Now, if you will procure for me a suit of clothes I can go directly and bring that money here—you shall be liberally compensated."

"Well, first I want to know what happened to you in the monastery. What caused them to treat you as they did?"

"The truth of it is I had the misfortune to overhear a conversation between Miguel Leonis, Father Jean and another party I need not mention. The subject of this conversation was treasonable to our French government. When they found out I knew, they accused me of having given information to the police, which is why they treated me as you have seen."

"This is hard to believe. Surely, there must have been more to it than that, or something of greater gravity. Whatever of treason was contained in their conversation, why would Father Jean then send you forth to publish it to the world? I want to be paid for my services to you, however, so I will get you the clothes and give you a chance to get the money."

When Jean Pierre was provided his new suit, he left the tavern and returned later in the day with an earth-stained package under his arm. Once back in his room, Ballade seated on the opposite side of the table, Jean Pierre opened his package and pulled out five neatly sealed packages, each labeled, "French Bank Bills, $10,000 francs."

"May the Lord help us," exclaimed Ballade, "Where in the world did these come from?"

"From the graveyard, from the tomb—don't ask any more questions, Ballade. Be satisfied that I have such a large sum of money I am well able to compensate you."

"May I open one of the packages?" asked the impressed Ballade.

"Certainly." Jean Pierre broke the seal of one of the packages and handed it over to Ballade for inspection.

"Infierno!" exclaimed Ballade. "What do you mean by treating me in this way? Do you think I am a fool?"

He shook the package out, scattering a flurry of neatly cut pieces of newspaper, each one cut to the dimensions of a French bank note. Jean Pierre turned pale. He was speechless as he hurriedly opened the second and the third, the fourth and the fifth packages. Each one contained nothing but old cut-up newspapers.

"So you have cheated me, you scoundrel," said the enraged Ballade. "I will turn you over to the police tomorrow. No, I will give you to a police officer now!" He rose to leave the room.

Jean Pierre begged Ballade to remain and hear him out while he explained how he himself had been cheated. This time, since he had nothing to gain otherwise, he told more of the story.

"I thought so," said Ballade when he had finished. "I told you there was something fishy about the story you told me about overhearing a conversation. They discovered you and knew you were going to open their strongbox—so they put these packages in place of good money, and you obliged by stealing them. When they found you to be a thief they just skinned you alive. They served you right.'"

"You can think that way if you want," answered John Peter. "I still have this new suit of clothes and you have fattened me up. So I was fooled. I thought this was money, it is trash. Ballade, just give me one more opportunity and I will have money, and I promise I will divide with you. I know how to get it, but not here. I need to go to Marseilles. Lend me enough now to enable me to reach Marseilles and I will send you— how much would you say your entertainment is worth.?"

"Well, it is worth one hundred twenty-five francs, and another one hundred for the suit of clothes—two hundred and twenty-five francs."

"When I get to Marseilles, I will send you five hundred," said Jean Pierre.

Ballade accepted the proposition, and the next day Jean Pierre boarded a train and rolled off for Marseilles.

Arriving there, he immediately called upon merchant Mascarel and presented to him a kindly letter from Father Jean, introducing "My Secretary, Friar Jean Pierre." In the letters were directions to Mascarel to provide a certain amount of money, part of which was to be used in a particular service at Marseilles and the remainder to be brought to the monastery at Cambo.

The money was immediately handed over to Jean Pierre and he departed. The letter he had written so closely imitated his former master's handwriting that it was beyond Mascarel's power of detection.

Some time later Mascarel answered the letter, expressing the pleasure it gave him to comply with the father superior's request and stating the amount of money furnished—five thousand francs.

Grave happenings within the walls of a monastery seldom find their way to the outer world, but when it became rumored around on the outside that Friar Jean Pierre had been degraded and cast out—all because he had discovered a treasonable conspiracy within the walls of the monastery—and that Miguel Leonis was the head of the conspiracy and that Jean Pierre had departed, had either been murdered or had fled the country, so it was that the monastery felt compelled to reveal the truth. The scandalous cause for his expulsion was then made known to the world.❧

15

Biscailuz and Mulligan—El Kanacka
John Robarts

ur history brings us back to California, where two Los Angeles lawyers were about to meet. Biscailuz[1] was a Basque whose successful sheep-herder father raised his son to become an American lawyer. He soared high in his profession yet groveled in the dust, because he had little ability. Along with his lack of ability was an attitude of towering assurance. Biscailuz liked to have the Basque people believe that he was a prodigy of their race—a lawyer speaking their own language, profoundly versed in California law and the American manner of doing courthouse business.

He had money at the time, having made $109,000 from the estate of a rich Basque whose will Biscailuz had written. Gaston Oxarart's entire estate had been devised to go to a nephew, and Biscailuz preyed upon that nephew for so long as he had a dollar. Why

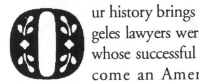

Martin V. Biscailuz

AVOCAT ET CONSEILLER EN LOIS

Examen d'Archives, de titres de propriétés, baux, contrats, hypothèques, etc., faits avec soin. Lettres écrites en Espagnol, Français, Anglais et Basque. Tenue des livres, Règlements de comptes. Recouvrements et collections opérés promptement.

Nos. 91, 92 et 93 Temple Block. Chez Smith, Brown et Hutton.

An advertisement by Martin Biscailuz in "L'Union Nouvelle, organe de la population Francaise du Sud de la Californie." January 27, 1883. Early Los Angeles had a large French population.

Los Angeles Public Library.

In the center, Main street, Los Angeles. On the right, the "Temple Block" where several of the lawyers in this story had their offices.

the nephew permitted himself to be thus imposed upon was not alto-gether clear. But the bank books showed that he had checked away to this lawyer the amount of money stated. Once Biscailuz got the money, he frequently got drunk and sharpers preyed upon him. He had a very great office in Temple Block,[2] a magnificent library—and no practice.

Early one morning, Biscailuz had just seated himself in his easy chair when Richard Mulligan, Esq., walked in. The lawyer who thus pre-sented himself was an odd fish indeed. He had a head shaped very much like an elongated gourd balanced at an angle of forty-five degrees, point-

Anson Brunson

Martin Biscailuz

J. G. Eastman

137

ing backward. His hair was brushed back and stood on end, making him look like a ground hog.

"Good morning, Dick," said Biscailuz. "How is everyone in Poverty Row?"—an allusion to the building where Mulligan kept his office—"Have you had a drink yet this morning?"

"Not yet," was the answer. "I came on some very important business. We can talk business first and drink afterward. To tell you the truth, I am as dry as a fish and poor as a church mouse."

"Well, I saw you yesterday at four o'clock and, from the way you talked and acted, you could have been Collis P. Huntington or Jay Gould. But then you are always high after four o'clock, Dick. Only when morning comes are you sometimes a decent man. Since it is still morning and you are decent, I will talk to you. But before we begin business I want to tell you that I have freed myself from your Poverty Club—those petifoggers and shysters in your building. They are forever preying upon me for four bits and a dollar and five dollars I have made up my mind to shake them. .For that matter, I propose to shake you, too."

"Before you shake me," Mulligan replied, "I have a business proposition for you. I want you to put me in the way of making a few thousand dollars—ten thousand dollars, maybe more. After I have made the money, Bisc, I will divide with you. I want you to shake the tree so I can gather the fruit as it falls to the ground."

"Yes, and you will eat it all, too. Precious little do I get of whatever comes into your clutches. I have heard of your tricks before, and experienced them myself on occasion. I have sent you valuable clients, Dick—out of whom you made money—all the while begging me for whiskey money. And I like a fool furnished it. When you collected your fee, you stayed out of my way. I never got a cent."

"Oh, well," said Mulligan, "those were small matters—twenty-five dollar, fifty dollar, a hundred-dollar fees. Much to me and nothing to you. You are rich, Bisc, and I belong to the Poverty Club, as you call it. But now to business. Let's dispatch it promptly so we may have a drink."

"What is it?"

"Leonis arrived here last night from Europe. Of course you know what happened up and around his ranch during his absence. The squatters piled in on him—on that eight-league Virgines ranch.[3] There was a battle royal and Banks, the chief of the squatters, got killed. Also several of Leonis' men, so perhaps it was fortunate for him that he was absent. The squatters are still there. Where one was killed, a half dozen have taken his place. Leonis can only get them off through the power of the law—I want to get that job, Bisc! It should be worth ten thousand dollars. I will divvy with you! I need for you to go to Leonis and tell him that I am the greatest lawyer in America. Tell him I have been a partner of Ben Butler, of Lyman Trumbull of Chicago, of Dan Voorhees. Just tell him I am the greatest lawyer of them all. For that matter, you can tell him I am the attorney-general of the United States! I can get those squatters off, tell him that, say I know all about it. Come on, Bisc, you can speak to him in his own language—he will listen to you. He will take your advice. Will you do it, Bisc?"

"Yes that might be worth trying you once more. This sounds like big business, although of course I can't be in on it openly. I will speak to Leonis as a disinterested person. I'll tell him I don't want any finger in the pie because of my youth and inexperience. And I'll tell him that his present lawyers put up that squatter job on him—to make money out of both him and the squatters—and I will convince him that you are the only honest lawyer in Los Angeles. The fact is, Dick, all lawyers are rascals, all of them pettifoggers, shysters, thieves—except for you and me, of course. That is the truth of it, and I will make Leonis believe it."

"When can you see him?"

"Just as soon as I find out where he is. Unless he is with old Mascarel. We must beware of Mascarel. Money is what we are after. I don't care anything about either the squatters or Miguel Leonis. All I want is the money, Dick, and to keep Mascarel out of this at least until we get the contract."

"Why don't we go downstairs and have a drink," suggested Mulligan. "I most emphatically agree with everything you have said, and

I hope you can make Leonis understand it as clearly as I do. Lend me a dollar, Bisc?"

"Never mind, Dick. I'll pay for the drinks," and the two left for Jake Phillippi's tap room,[4] where they stood before the counter.

"I will have whiskey," said Mulligan.

"Give me some absinthe," Bisc ordered, and he rolled his eyes heavenward. The eyes of Richard Mulligan, being on the top of his head, seemed always to be pointing in that direction.

"Now, Bisc," said Mulligan, "you must hurry up about this business. Mustn't let the grass grow under your feet. That lawyer John Robarts will be after Miguel, so you must get there ahead of him. But then Robarts sleeps late in the morning. I get up early, you know—the early bird catches the worm."

"You're not after worms, Dick. You get up early so you can bum a drink. It's the whiskey you're after."

"That may be true," Mulligan conceded. "So, as long as you've mentioned it, I believe I will take another. Can you stand another, Bisc?"

"Not until after I see Leonis. I must go—don't detain me here."

"Well then, lend me a dollar."

"No, I told you I've sworn off being preyed upon like this."

"I know that—but this new deal of ours makes it different. Lend me a dollar, Bisc, I will pay you the next time I see you."

"I know you will. You will pay me by asking me for still another dollar. I remember when it used to be five dollars, Dick, then two. Now you are reduced to one. Next you'll be asking for four bits?"

"If you succeed in getting this contract from Leonis, I'll borrow a hundred dollars from you!"

"All right, here's the dollar. I am off to find Leonis."

After Biscailuz left, Mulligan had another drink and then sallied out toward the street. As he passed the reception area of the block, he encountered John Robarts and invited him into the tap room for a drink.

After swallowing his whiskey, Mulligan turned to Robarts and said, "John, do you have a dollar on you? I had forgotten that I am entirely without change. I will hand it to you the next time we meet."

"Look here, Dick, I'm getting tired of this. You have been borrowing from me for a long time. When you started it was five dollars, and you kept coming down until now you're at the dollar mark. If I give you a dollar, will you quit?!"

"Certainly, Mr. Robarts, if you say so—although I don't know why I should stop when I am working up some big business that I propose to take you in on. I want you because of your superior command of the Spanish language. It is my misfortune to speak and understand only English. For this great case that I am working up, I will furnish the brain and all you need to do is supply me with the Spanish language."

"And money to get drunk on, I suppose," said Robarts, handing the gentleman a dollar. "The next time you invite me to have a drink, kindly tell me beforehand that you expect me to pay for it. How is the Poverty Club getting along, Dick? You must be president of it by now."

"Well, now, don't be in a such a hurry, John. Let's have another drink. It is getting on twelve o'clock. Let's sit down here and talk this thing over—this case I am starting on. Have you any news about Leonis?"

"No."

"I believe your firm represents him legally and that you are his attorney. Where is he?"

"He'll be here in a week or two—or within a month if he overstays his time. He had said he would be back in three months and the time is pretty nearly up. At the most, it would be four."

"And you can't do anything until he comes back?"

"Not that I know of. We haven't been paid any money. Mascarel won't put up a dollar, and you know lawyers work for money. But when old Miguel gets back he will shell out those twenty-dollar gold pieces like grain pouring from a ruptured sack. We will give them fits, those squatters on the Virgines. Just you wait and see," said Robarts as he rose to take his departure.

"We must have another drink before you go," Mulligan said hurriedly. "How I wish, Robarts, that you would take me into this Leonis

141

business. You know I can help you. You are a young lawyer and I am an old lawyer." They ordered another round of drinks. Mulligan was detaining Robarts as long as possible for fear he might learn of Leonis' arrival, before Biscailuz could work him.

"Besides," Mulligan continued, "You are not in a hurry. And we are getting along so nicely. You have nothing in court today, and neither have I. John, I really wish you would cut loose from those partners of yours. They are great rascals, every one of them. And they have no ability, not one bit—excepting maybe Jim Eastman—but he is drunk all the time. Cut loose from them, John, and let's you and I go into partnership."

"Well, Dick, I will certainly consider the proposition."

"Hmmmm—have you a spare dollar on you?"

"I just gave you a dollar!"

"You did?"

"Do you just ask out of force of habit?"

"You didn't give me a dollar—and I haven't a nickel," said Mulligan, feeling in his pockets. "You will have to pay for these drinks anyway because I don't have a cent. Oh, by the way, I just saw Brunson this morning and he told me that if I were to meet you I should send you immediately to his office. He said he has some important business with you and that he tried to find you all day yesterday—and when he did, it was five o'clock and you were blind drunk. He said to me, 'If I can't see him before twelve I don't want to see him at all, because I know he will be half seas over after that hour and drunk as usual by four o'clock.'"

Mulligan rang the little bell on their table and the whiskey slinger approached.

"How many drinks have we had?"

"Eight drinks," said the waiter. "It's eight drinks for a dollar, you know."

"Mr. Robarts will pay you," Mulligan said, and he walked into the hall and disappeared.

Robarts paid the bill and hurried off to find Brunson. Brunson did not actually want anything of Robarts—this was Mulligan's ploy to keep Robarts out of the way so he would not meet Leonis in the street or hear about his arrival.

Brunson's law office was in the same building, Temple Block. Mulligan posted himself on the opposite side of the street so he could observe whether Robarts went up the stairs to the lawyer's office. Finding that he did, Mulligan then rushed off to his own office at the Poverty Club, where he found El Kanacka.

"Go over to Brunson's office and find John Robarts," Mulligan told him. "If he is not in the office, he will be coming away from there. When you find him, tell him that Judge Sepulveda wants to see him immediately on some important court business. Then you walk with him down to the judge's chambers."

The Kanacka did as he was instructed. He walked into Brunson's office, where he found Brunson and Robarts engaged in trivial conversation principally related to escapades in the feminine world. The Kanacka offered to wait outside.

"No, sit down, Mr. Kanacka," he was told, and he sat down and joined the conversation, keeping it going as long as he could. When Robarts was about to leave, the Kanacka informed him that he had brought a message from Judge Sepulveda, that the Judge wanted to see him about some business then on his calendar.

"He said for me not to lose sight of you until you appeared at his chambers," the Kanacka told him. All of this was a subterfuge to divert Robarts from possibly encountering Leonis. By now it was the noon hour and the judge had gone to his lunch.

"Well," said the Kanacka, "I know the judge lunches at Nick Mercadantes'—at the Queen. Let's go there." And so they went.

The judge was not there, but Robarts said they might as well sit down and have lunch themselves—an invitation El Kanacka would not think to decline.

By this time, Robarts had become oblivious to mundane things. He ordered a cocktail before lunch, and then El Kanacka ordered another cocktail. When lunch came, they both ordered beer and then another cocktail. They did more drinking than eating, until Robarts became so drowsy he laid his head upon the table and fell asleep.

El Kanacka stood up to leave and informed Mercadantes as to the condition of Robarts, with the admonition that he should take care of him. "He is a good fellow and has plenty of money. He will pay for everything." With that, El Kanacka reported back to Mulligan that Robarts had been disposed of for the day.

By four o'clock, Mulligan himself was booming drunk. At five o'clock he was blind drunk. But early the next morning he soaked his head in a basin of water, and was as sober and clear-headed as a judge when he sallied forth to find Biscailuz.

The sun had not yet risen when Mulligan, who liked to walk, ambled in the direction of Boyle Heights[5] to see Biscailuz at his residence. As he arrived at the house, Biscailuz stuck out his head in the morning sun.

"Well, hello, Dick! You here? Are you after the worm or the whiskey this morning?"

"Hello, Bisc. First the worm and we can have the whiskey later on. Do you have any news? Did you see Leonis?"

"No. He arrived on the evening train and went directly to Escorpion the same night. I saw Mascarel."

"What in the devil did you do that for! Didn't I tell you to keep out of Mascarel's sight? If he gets on to us, he will ruin all our plans. Leonis is absolutely under his influence."

"I saw Mascarel to pump him for information, to find out what Leonis is going to do and when he will be back from his ranch."

"Well, what did you find out?"

"Leonis left Los Angeles in a great hurry. He was going to find out who were to blame for the squatter fight, and he was going to make it hot for them. He suspects his lawyers of encouraging the squatters in going there—taking small fees from these squatters and then encouraging Leonis' men to make war on them. Mascarel is satisfied as to the circumstances of the case, but will let Leonis find out for himself. I also learned that Mascarel has employed Brunson to eject the squatters from Las Virgines, and it is very probable that Leonis will accept Mascarel's judgment and keep Brunson. What are we going to do, Dick?"

"Do? Why, you must be at the Escorpion before the sun reaches noon. Your father was a great friend of Leonis, so you, acting the part of an impartial friend and lawyer, can influence him as you choose. Say that Brunson is the biggest rascal in California. Tell him he sells out his clients and uses them like shuttlecocks, all for the purpose of getting their money. Tell him how Brunson served the San Fernando people, Maclay and the others, and then say that he is drunk more than half the time."

Mulligan continued, "Make him believe it, Bisc! Tell him I am the attorney-general of the United States! And that I have all of that squatter business in the palm of my hand. Make him think that he would be acquiring an influential U.S. officer for his suit and that it is to be a great secret—one that he must not mention even to Mascarel. If the news should leak out, you can say that he has subsidized the attorney-general of the United States—an offense that might ruin him, for he would lose his land grant—but tell him that if he keeps it to himself, everything will come out well. You can also tell him that, as far as I am concerned, there shall be no fee charged until the case is won. Now, how soon can you start? There is twenty-thousand dollars in it for you, Bisc. By the way, have you got a dollar you can lend me?"

"Oh, get out!"

"Well, I can't get along this morning without a dollar. I haven't had a drink yet and I am just dying. Give me a dollar, Bisc. I promise to hand it back the next time I see you."

"Oh, all right. Here's your dollar. Now, go over to Jake's and fill yourself. Just don't speak to me again until tomorrow morning. I will be at the Escorpion at noon today. I will see you tomorrow."

145

Mulligan shuffled his way off the front lawn of Biscailuz' house and walked hurriedly back to town. As he walked, he fished out several coins from his pocket and counted carefully. He had a total of four dollars and fifty cents.☙

Endnotes

1. Martin Biscailuz was a key figure in southern California's Basque colony as well as in Los Angeles society. Born in California and educated in Europe, he was fluent in the Basque language and held a virtual monopoly on the legal business of Basques in the region. He is reported to have amassed a personal fortune of $100,000 while still a young man. Rumors that he had mishandled millionaire Simon Oxarart's estate caused him to lose the Basque trade, and by the mid-'90s he drank excessively and was in dire straits. Tried twice for defauding clients, he served a short sentence in prison. (*Amerikanuak*, p. 336, see illustration.)

2. Temple Block was a three-story commercial building constructed in 1858 by John Temple. At the time, all big buildings in Los Angeles were referred to as blocks. In *Fortune Favors The Brave* is a description of this site where Horace Bell maintained his law offices for years. "Located at the junction of Main, Spring and Temple streets, the three-story building stood in the commercial center on the north apex of a triangular block, the site of the present City Hall, and faced all three streets. The first building back of its south walls and separated from it by a short street was the courthouse." (p. 285, footnote 6)

3. During the late 1870s and 1880s, Americans poured into Southern California and a number tried to homestead on disputed land on and surrounding El Escorpion. The Las Virgenes area west of Calabasas be-

came a war zone. The situation is described in *Cattle On The Conejo:* ". . . an old grant (Virgines) had been partly divided among some of the heirs before California became a state. Some of these titles were validated (by the U.S. Land Commission) and some were not. Later, part of this grant was thrown open to public entry, and the settlers came in. There was friction with the former owners, but it did not become serious until a man known as The Basco (Leonis) appeared upon the scene. He was a man of means and offered money to the original owners of the grant for the land as well as for whatever rights they still fancied they owned. They accepted the offer. The Basco was a unique character. Strong as a bull physically, he was filled with a determination to clear out the squatters." (p.28)

4. Los Angeles newsman William A. Spalding recalled Jake Philippi's tap room with sentiment: "On the Court street side of the (Temple) block, facing south, were the bill-posting and distributing headquarters of McLain & Lehman and the beer saloon of Jake Philippi. The latter comprised a capacious barroom and an adjoining lounging room, with round tables and plenty of chairs, and the floor always covered with clean sawdust. There was also a patent 'melodeon' or music box, of wonderful German workmanship, into which a customer could slip a piece of money, and it helped to while away the time. And, with the clean floor, the easy seat, a pretzel or two, or a little German 'snack'— rye bread and a few thin slices of bologna or liverwurst, and a pot of mustard, with a mug of beer on the side—it wasn't so bad."

5. Boyle Heights, on the east side of the Los Angeles River, was an early suburb of the city. The subdivision was laid out in 1876.

Leonis

16

Espiritu and Odon Feel Betrayed
A Squatter War in Hidden Hills—Las Virgenes
Land Controversey

Leonis had been absent from his ranch about ten weeks, and upon his return he found a pretty kettle of fish. No sooner had he been out of sight than the plotting commenced against him. The Domecs became intensely intimate with Espiritu and Odon, and they worked upon Col. Andres Larios y Pacheco. Soon the consensus of them all was that Leonis was a great rascal—that he had laid plans to ruin every man, woman and child in and around the country who had in any manner come in contact with him, either in business or socially. They decided his intention was, as soon as he got back, to pack the entire Indian outfit—Odon and Espiritu and their kinspeople that he had been supporting—to San Fernando and dump them there. Clearly, he had prevailed upon Odon to deed him the Escorpion. As for Espiritu, he had had her services, subjecting her to a condition of servitude worse than slavery, without paying her a cent.

Now it is a fact that Indians were easily imposed upon. So long as Leonis was present and around, Espiritu and Odon were all right—but as soon as he was absent and could not speak for himself, they believed every evil thing said about him. He was, they contended, the most mendacious of men. First off, Odon jumped upon him with a lawsuit to set aside his deed to the Escorpion, on the ground that it had been obtained

149

Espiritu Leonis, c. 1826 – 1906 (taken c. 1879).

fraudulently. That is to say, he claimed Leonis had cheated him out of his ranch. Espiritu was convinced to sue Leonis for one-half of the ranch stock—cattle and sheep—and claim that she had merely taken Leonis in as an assistant and a herder—that he had contributed nothing to the general accumulation because it had come from her capital.

  The Domecs beat the bushes for squatters to jump the Virgines. Domec was acquainted with a number of Americans, and he was well-informed as to the character of Leonis' title—that it was worthless. It required very little investigation on the part of the squatting community to realize that the United States government had relegated the eight leagues to the public domain. This made it unsurveyed government land. Hence, within less than a month after Leonis' departure, about forty squatters moved onto the Virgines lands. Every eligible location had an American upon it, and they fully intended to stay. After the Americans settled in, Domec used his persuasive powers on Colonel Pacheco to incite a crowd to go over there and whip the squatters off. He told Pacheco this would make him especially solid with Leonis upon his return.

The colonel was a very bombastic character—fond of applause and a great exaggerator of his own prowess and former achievements. Finding this a campaign to his liking, Pacheco and Manuel Dominguez started to raise an army—promising large bounties and gratuities from Leonis upon his return if the men succeeded in ejecting the squatters. Having succeeded in getting twenty-five or thirty dare-devil Mexicans to join the enterprise, their plan of operation was to take the squatters in detail. The squatters lived at distances apart, one man on a quarter section covering a spring and another a mile distant on a second quarter section covering a grove of oak timber, another on a rich alluvial flat and so on.

Massing their forces at the Escorpion, Pacheco and Dominguez marched over and took position at Calabasas, intending to send out detached parties to gather in the squatters—all to be disarmed, of course, when arrested.

The leader of the squatters, a man named Banks, had seen a great deal of military service.[1] He had been distinguished as a scout in the federal army during the Civil War, and he knew what he was about. While Colonel Pacheco was making his dispositions at Calabasas, Banks and his squatters were conveniently near, so that the first detachment sent out got promptly taken in as prisoners of war. Pacheco underestimated the strength of his opponent and ordered an advance. A bushwhacking fight ensued. It was a very bloody affair, that battle at Calabasas. Banks was mortally wounded and several other squatters were killed outright. On Colonel Pacheco's side, a great number were made to bite the dust. Victory rested on the banner of the squatters, however, and the Mexicans were disastrously routed.

The wounded Banks was brought to Los Angeles, where he died and was buried. Others got disposed of in the usual way—they were buried somewhere. The attempt to evict them made the American squatters very bitter.

When Leonis returned, he immediately started to straighten out the entanglements. Fortunately, Espiritu had not yet gone into court, although she had paid a liberal retainer to a lawyer. Odon had actually commenced his suit.

Leonis began with Espiritu. He brought her to town to see the banker Hellman. There, to her surprise, she learned that before Leonis departed for the Pyrenees he had deposited twenty-thousand dollars in Hellman's bank—to be used for her behalf and benefit in the event of Leonis' death during his proposed trip or his inability to return to Los Angeles. This opened the woman's eyes as to the deceit that had been practiced upon her by the vilifiers of Leonis. She became satisfied that he was acting as her best friend, despite all that had been said and done, and that he had been and would continue to be the best friend of her father. Returning to the ranch, Espiritu tried to undo that which had been done.

The suit of Odon, however, had been pushed with vigor, and the cause came before the courts, with the taking of depositions and the examination of witnesses—Espiritu herself being the principal witness as to the dealings between Leonis and her father. She made a clean breast of the whole thing. The lawyers tried to make out that she was the wife of Leonis. This she absolutely repudiated, stating that she was his servant, his housekeeper, nothing more, nothing less.

The Domecs stood behind Odon and pushed him forward. When Leonis' lawyers came to examine the deed, they confessed the document was void—for want of description. Espiritu, who was very smart, suggested a compromise to her father, that he should deed the ranch to her and she would do the right thing by Leonis. Also, Odon would be treated as before, remaining comfortably supported for the rest of his natural life.

Thus that end of the tangle was straightened out, but the more serious one was the on-going squatter question at the Virgines. Calabasas is three miles from the Escorpion ranch house. At the time, Calabasas was simply some springs and a few garden patches that the Indians cultivated. It was considered a part of the Virgines ranch.

Through Mascarel, Brunson had been retained and liberally fee'd to report on the Virgines title and the feasibility of ejecting the squatters through the medium of the courts. He reported back to Mascarel and Leonis that the Virgines was an eight-league valid grant to Apolonio Dominguez, made in 1834. At the time, all the requirements of the Mexican law had been complied with and the title was a perfect one. Then, in 1851 or '52 the United States Land Commission was appointed by Congress to investigate the Spanish and Mexican land grants in California, and the law provided that all claimants under either Spain or Mexico should file their claims before the United States Land Commission prior to a certain date in 1855, under penalty of their ranches being relegated to the public domain.

Because the Dominguez people did not present their claim to the land commission, by due operation of law, the grant was relegated to the public domain and became a part thereof. "However," said Brunson, "a treaty between the United States and Mexico—the treaty of Guadalupe Hidalgo—had guaranteed that all parties holding valid claims under Mexico should be protected under the government of the United States. Since Domiguez had a valid and perfect grant, it should not have been necessary for him to present it to the land commission," Brunson argued. "The land commission could not make his title better and they could not make it worse. Further, the treaty between the two national powers was superior and paramount to an act of Congress, and therefore the Dominguez title to the Virgines was perfect—and Leonis, having succeeded to that title, was the perfect, valid and legitimate owner of that land."

Brunson contracted to eject the squatters, for which service he demanded a certain amount of money and a large tract of land—both of which were conceded by Leonis.[2]

Let us return now to Biscailuz after his trip to the Escorpion, which occurred the day after Leonis went home. Biscailuz came back to Los Angeles that night—and bright and early the following morning he found Richard Mulligan, Esq., standing upon his front porch.

"Hello, Dick! You are after the worm,[3] are you?" exclaimed Biscailuz, smiling as he stepped outside to where the great lawyer was seated.

"Yes, I want the worm—I want to know about your interview with Leonis. Did you see him?"

"Yes."

"And what did he say?"

"He listened to what I had to say but wouldn't say anything back. Only that he would be along in a day or two to see Mascarel. And that Mascarel had suggested he use Brunson."

"Did you tell him what a scoundrel Brunson is?"

"Of course I did, but of course Mascarel would give Brunson a different character. Dick, you had better go see Brunson yourself early this morning. Perhaps you can worm yourself into the case through him."

"Have you a spare dollar, Bisc?"

"Yes, Dick. But see Brunson first. He is usually at his office at nine o'clock."

"But Bisc, I want some breakfast. I am hungry. I didn't eat anything yesterday and I want some breakfast. Give me that spare dollar."

"Well, all right, here it is, Dick—but only on your promise to go and get a good square meal, and don't drink anything until you have seen and talked with Brunson."

Mulligan left Biscailuz at the house and walked back to town. He was at the counter of Jake Philippi's, eating slices of bologna, when

Haley came in.

Haley was a lawyer, a liberal good-hearted fellow who drank only if he could find someone to drink with him—so he said, "Hello, Dick! Will you have a drink?"

"Don't mind if I do," said Mulligan. "Haley, have you got a spare dollar?"

To save his life, Hailey could not refuse such a request. He handed over the dollar—and Dick returned to his sausage.

"What is the news, Haley? You are one of Leonis' lawyers. He says you got up that squatter riot at Calabasas during his absence. He is after you, Haley."

"That is all humbug, Dick. Have another drink?"

"Don't mind if I do. Oh! Haley, I wish you would let me have another dollar. I have to file an answer in court this morning and it takes two dollars. I just lack a dollar now to make it up. Let me have it, please. I was just joking about the Calabasas business. Leonis never said any such thing, as far as I know, but if you will lend me another dollar I will find out what he does say."

Haley lent him the other dollar and took his departure. After Richard Mulligan finished his breakfast off the sausage tray, he walked out onto the street and spied Brunson. Brunson was in his buggy, having just driven in from his ranch in the suburbs.

Mulligan followed him to the stable where he kept his team. "Brunson, my dear fellow, how are you? I have some very important business with you that I prefer to discuss in your office. Are you going there?"

"Yes, directly."

Brunson removed his duster and his gloves, and the two started walking to Temple Block and soon were quietly ensconced in Brunson's back room.

"Oh, Dick, will you have a smile with me?"

Brunson had a sideboard and it was covered with brandy bottles.

"I don't mind if I do, Brunson. I haven't had a drink this morning," and the two had a glass of brandy.

"Now," Mulligan began, "let me tell you what I want with you. I don't know Leonis, and I understand that he has employed you to remove the squatters from the Virgines. I have been working on that case, Brunson. Some of Leonis' friends have been after me ever since the battle. Now I know you are a great lawyer—yes, the greatest lawyer in California. That is conceded by all parties. And I very much like your methods, Brunson. You are straightforward, you never beat around the bush, and you are honest. Many lawyers I know, of otherwise great ability, I wouldn't have a case with under any circumstances. But you, Brunson, I want you to take me into the case. Now, I don't care what you get in the way of a fee—you can give me just whatever you please. Let me tell you confidentially that I have some inside tracks on that squatter business that you cannot get along well without. And I don't want you, when you file your compliant against the squatters, to enter my name so it's Brunson & Mulligan. No, just let me work with you. I will not be an attorney of record, you shall be the sole attorney of record. I just want to work with you, and you may pay me what you please."

Brunson was a very great lawyer—perhaps the greatest of his day. He had his faults, and his faults were many, but he was a generous, good fellow. Brunson could not refuse a favor to any one who asked it.

He said, "Why, yes, Dick, I would like to have you help me in that case and I will enter you on the complaint, as my associate attorney."

"No, I don't want it that way," answered Richard Mulligan, Esq. "I prefer it the way I said. But of course I will expect you to do the fair thing by me. I will leave it all to you, Brunson. If you get twenty thousand dollars for the case, you might at least give me one or two thousand—but you need not do that unless you think I earned it."

"All right," said Brunson. "We are agreed. Now I have to get ready to go to court, Dick. Please excuse me, I have got to get some papers together."

Mulligan left and went directly to the office of Biscailuz, where he addressed him in good spirits, "I have seen Brunson and I got the worm as well, Bisc."

"You look as if you have got several worms since I last saw you. Did you spend all of the dollar I gave you?"

"No, not a cent of it."

"But you have had several drinks—I can tell by the way your mouth sticks out. It's peculiar, Dick, how whiskey-drinking affects some persons. Some get red noses, others blood-shot eyes. You show neither, but when you are drunk or even half full, Dick, both your chin and your mouth stick out—projecting forward like the prow of a modern warship. Well, what does Brunson say?"

"He says he has been retained to eject the squatters from the Virgines, and he is going to take me in."

"What about the fee. He divides his fee with you?"

"No, he is just going to work with me. You know, Bisc, I have been specially employed by Leonis."

"How so? When?"

"Why, through you, of course. Didn't Leonis agree yesterday that if Brunson would take me in he would give me twenty thousand dollars? And has not Brunson done so?"

"I suppose one could say that is what he agreed to," said Biscailuz.

"Of course I could, and I will, if necessary—no trouble about that. Now, look Bisc. I am going to help Brunson run this thing and not say a word to Leonis except to ask him for information. I intend to busy myself and do a great deal of talking. Then, when we have ejected the squatters, I propose to claim twenty thousand dollars from Leonis on a separate contract, and I want you to swear me through."

"Well, that is all right with me—but I want some guarantee that I will get my divvy."

"You will, Bisc, you will. Now. have you got a spare dollar?"

"Oh, get out."

"I am going to call on you in a day or two for that hundred! Lend me the dollar now and I will pay it back the next time I see you."

With visions of ten thousand dollars before him, Biscailuz made the transfer of a round solid dollar. Two hours later, Richard Mulligan,

157

Esq., was booming drunk, without having spent a cent of his own money throughout the day. He saved up dollars as a miser saves his pennies. He was indeed an odd fish.∽

Endnotes

1. While the names "Pacheco" and "Domiguez" have not been verified, Banks was a real person and the battle did happen.

2. This may or may not be the particular case, but it is a good opportunity to quote the following story from *Graves: My Seventy Years In California.*

     "Some lawyer, I forget who, now, sued Don Miguel Leonis, litigious Basque sheep-owner, for a twenty-five thousand dollar fee for services rendered. He was trying his own case before a jury, and faring badly. Col. Jim Howard, by chance, came into the court room. the plaintiff, who was his own lawyer, in desperation, without consulting Howard, put him on the stand to prove the value of his services. He stated what he had done for Leonis, and asked Howard if, in his opinion, $25,000 was a fair compensation for services rendered. Howard replied, "My practice has been of such a vagabond, beggarly nature, that I am hardly in your class, but if I should earn a $25,000 fee, I would die of heart failure, but, knowing you and your legal ability, and knowing the litigious character of Don Miguel, I cannot realize any services that you could have rendered him that would be worth over two dollars and a half, unless you had killed him, then, by a stretch of your conscience, you might have charged him five dollars."

3. "After the worm" almost surely means that Mulligan was thirsting for a drink of Absinthe, a bitter green liqueur that was made, at least in those days, with "wormwood," a plant that added to the bitter flavor. Tradi-

tion has it that addiction to Absinthe (because of the wormwood content) leads to insanity. Bell seems to hint that Biscailuz was fond of Absinthe. Read elsewhere about Biscailuz' fate.

Leonis

17

Mulligan and Biscailuz Enter the Fray

In accordance with his contract with Mascarel and Leonis, Brunson commenced an action in the proper court against the squatters on the Virgines. Prior to appearing in court, however, the lawyer approached the judge, who, by the way, was Mexican. Once the legal situation was explained—and having great respect for the solemnity of treaties and the superior learning and legal good sense of Brunson—the judge fully agreed with him. The outlook was very favorable that the squatters would be ejected.

The action became a bombshell. It stunned the squatters and astonished all intelligent, unbiased Americans who held a high respect for acts of Congress—the U.S. Congress having relegated these lands to the public domain. They were even more astounded by Brunson's audacity. But who cared for public opinion so long as the judge agreed with the lawyer?

As soon as the action was filed, Mulligan called for his silent partner, El Kanacka.[1]

"Raf," he said, "you know a good many of those squatters at the Virgines, don't you?"

"Oh, yes, I know most of them. Branscomb's now the boss there."

"Get a horse, Raf, and go to the Virgines as quick as you can. Find all of those squatters and tell them of the suit. So there may be no mistake about it, I will furnish you with a copy of the complaint, they will be summoned within a week. Tell the squatters that I am the man to defend them in this suit, that I have the inside track on Leonis and I know how to handle him. You can say that Brunson is just bluffing—and that he has no case. Tell them he is only bleeding Leonis and Mascarel, and that I know all about it. Mascarel tried to employ me before he went to Brunson, you can tell them that."

Mulligan warmed to his subject and continued, "Tell them that Leonis and Mascarel offered me ten thousand dollars to take this case and eject the squatters, but that I refused—because I am an honest, conscientious American. You can say I once was a squatter myself, a grubber in the ground, until my innate talents sprouted, grew and bloomed. Then the great lawyers of the country took me up, educated me and made me a partner. I know more in one minute than Brunson ever knew in his life. Don't forget to say what a thief and a shyster Brunson is, a prince of pettifoggers. Also say that I know they are poor and I don't expect much—although we still must get all we can out of them, Raf. Tell them I always take the side of the weak and oppressed."

Within a very few days, a squatter delegation came to Los Angeles from the seat of war. El Kanacka, who had been lying in wait for them, conducted the group to the headquarters of the Poverty Club—that is, the office of Richard Mulligan, Esq. A business discussion immediately ensued.

"How many are you in all—settlers?"

"We number about forty, even told. Now, what will you charge to take our case? You know it means so much per capita."

"I could not say at this moment," answered Mulligan, "although the law is on your side—without question—this will be a big fight, a bitter fight, with piles of money against us. I'll tell you what I will do, gentlemen. If you pay me a retainer, I will thoroughly investigate and brief the case, and give you my written opinion. Then we can make terms. But I want a reasonable retainer, and I will want to use some money preliminarily. When I have given you my written opinion, which will accompany my brief, if we should fail to agree on a final contract, you will have had the benefit of my advice and my opinion, even if you do not employ me."

"What is a retainer?" inquired the spokesman of the committee.

"Well, a retainer means that you will pay me so much down, cash, today."

"Yes, I understand now. About how much do you want, Mr. Mulligan?"

"Well, say two hundred dollars. That is five dollars per head."

"Then should you decided to take the case, how much additional would we have to pay?"

"Oh, we won't quarrel about that. We will see what ability your people have to pay. I always stand in with the settlers, whether they pay me or not, and I wouldn't ask a cent from you now, except I have to fight the most rascally gang that ever infested any country in the world. Brunson is a concoctor of perjury, Mascarel and Leonis have barrels of money and the stake they are fighting for, the Virgines ranch, is worth hundreds of thousands of dollars. But we must go to work. There is no time for delay, gentlemen. When can you pay me the two hundred dollars?"

"We can pay you immediately, Mr. Mulligan. We held a meeting when Mr. Kanacka went up there, and at that meeting we collected five dollars from each settler, with some extra money to pay contingent expenses. So, with the concurrence of the committee, we will pay you your retainer."

The committee concurred and two hundred dollars was passed over to the great attorney. When the committee suggested a receipt for the money, Richard Mulligan, Esq., acted very insulted by the reflection upon his high character.

"I will go to work on your case today. In fact, I have been working on it for weeks. I will embody my notes in a written brief and an opinion, which will be ready by the time the summons is served. Then I will still have ten days in which to appear."

After some further informal discussion, the chairman said to Mr. Mulligan, "Do you ever drink?"

"Very seldom," answered Mulligan. "Of all men in the world lawyers ought to keep sober—any man who drinks is sure to become sloppy at some time. A clear, cool head is what carries a lawyer through, if he has the natural ability and the cultured intellect necessary for the profession. I don't like to be seen in saloons, but they do have some private rooms at the Reception and a private entrance to them. If you gentlemen will go through the bar room, Raf will conduct you to these rooms and I will enter privately. I will be more than happy to join you."

So the attorney and his clients adjourned to the Reception Saloon, which was situated in Temple Block, at the opposite end from Jake Phillippi's. On their way they ran into Biscailuz.

"Hello, Dick," he said. "Where are you going?"

"A private word if you please, Bisc," Mulligan said, pulling him aside. "Please don't address me that way in the presence of such honorable clients. That is to say, Bisc, these fellows came down from the Calabasas to get me to take the squatters' side of the fight—you know, the one with Mascarel, Leonis and Brunson, the three thieves. What do you think about it?"

"I think it is all right if they will put up the money. Get as much as you can, Dick, but remember, I am to have a divvy."

"Oh, certainly. Have you a spare dollar, Bisc? Raf has taken them to the bar room at the Reception and I am going in the private way, to one of the back rooms. I want to wet them up a little. It will cost me about a dollar. Lend me the dollar—I'll give it back the next time I see you—and you might come along. Only don't say anything to them unless it 'boosts' me."

Biscailuz went in with him, and they all met in the back room of the Reception, where Mulligan ordered the drinks.

"Whiskey straight for me. Gentlemen, what will you have?"

The gentlemen all took beer; Bisc wanted some absinthe. As the gentlemen talked, the principal direction of their conversation was the villification of Brunson. This came from Mulligan, and the others heartily concurred. Then they all denounced Leonis, "He ought to be shot. He ought to be treated exactly like the settlers handled More. They ought to just take him out and shoot him."

The unfortunate More in question had objected to squatters taking his land from him, for which they deemed he should die. Most any man should be killed who objects to being robbed, and so they murdered More.

From the legal actions of Leonis and Mascarel and their lawyer Brunson, it looked as though they were going to object to being robbed, and so Mulligan proposed that the fair thing to do was to kill the whole batch—if only it could be done without exciting too much notice.

"I mean, only if you can make a private job of it, gentlemen. But for goodness sake, don't permit it to be suspected that I ever heard such talk! But you won't kill them. No! No! No! Not necessary! Not necessary, gentlemen! I will kill them! I will kill them in the courts, metaphorically. I will mop up the courtroom floor with them, especially with Brunson for I owe him a grudge. Oh, Biscailuz, have you got a spare dollar? I have no change, gentlemen, therefore I have to call on my friend, Mr. Biscailuz. Please excuse me. Hand over the dollar, Bisc. I will give it back to you the next time we meet."

The chairman of the delegation interrupted: "Oh, no, never mind—I will pay this," and by that time they had drunk another round, which took pretty nearly two dollars to pay.

Mulligan was very profuse in his thanks. "Gentlemen," he announced, "I will make it all right the next time we meet."

After further discussion and a few more rounds, Mulligan's jaw started to elongate, and El Kanacka thought it about time to adjourn the meeting. He marshaled the Calabasans into the bar room and, in Spanish, requested Biscailuz to get Mulligan out through the private entrance, out of sight of the committee. Biscailuz took the hint and helped Mulligan upstairs to his office.

"Dick," he told him, "you are getting yourself into a bad fix. You have committed yourself to Brunson to help Leonis. Through me, you claim a private contract with Leonis for twenty thousand dollars, and now you are fishing for small coin from these squatters. Have they paid you anything, Dick? If so, I want the divvy."

"Not a cent," said Mulligan, "I don't want anything from them. Couldn't take anything if I did want it. I am coquetting with them, that is all. I want to use them in Leonis' interest. I want to find out all their secrets. Of course, I wouldn't dare take their money —that would be contrary to professional ethics. You know, Bisc, we must uphold the honor of the profession. We can't afford to lower ourselves to the level of Brunson, Jim Eastman, John Robarts and such professional trash—men who are eternally scheming to beat someone out of money. When I take a man's money, Bisc, I fight for him to the last gasp. I couldn't take a cent from those poor fellows, even if I thought I could successfully defend them. It will be with a great many qualms of professional conscience that I claim twenty thousand dollars from Leonis on that special contract you made with him, because he has got to be beaten. He is being buncoed by Brunson. But still, Bisc, we are in for it. Have you a spare dollar?"

"I wish I had a revolver, loaded, so I could give you a spare bullet, Dick. If there is any one in the world who deserves to be shot, it is you! The way you are going, it will not be long before you are called 'Drunken Dick'—and when you go for that 'spare dollar' all you will get is a spare kick. I wish I were big enough to kick you now. If I were, I would kick you down onto the sidewalk. Where's the dollar I gave you a little while ago?"

"Well, the truth is, Bisc, I have it in my pocket—but I have to file an answer today. It is my last day in a very important case, and I have to have two dollars. I only lack one dollar now, you know. It is a very important case, Bisc. If you will give me the dollar, I will take you into the case. There's money in it, and if I don't get my answer filed it will be a default—and that wouldn't do for a lawyer of my professional reputation. I know you think it pretty hard of me, Bisc, but you have lots of money.

You have just bushels of it since Oxarart died. You can easily spare me a dollar. Then I will let you go on that hundred dollars I said you should lend me."

Biscailuz handed him the dollar and left. Mulligan stood up, slid down the stairs and wobbled his way into Jake Philippi's.๛

Endnotes

1. "El Kanacka" was apparently a nickname for Eugenio Rafael Plummer, commonly called "Rafael" or "Raf." Born in 1853, he lived to be 90, and spent his last years in the Plummer House, which used to be in Plummer Park, West Hollywood, but in 1983 was moved to the Leonis Adobe grounds to save from demolition the part that had not already been lost to vandalism and fire. Built about 1874, it is California Landmark #160.

The Leonis and Plummer families were acquainted. In Juan Menendez' diary appears (translated from the Spanish) "The 13th of March, 1877 Rafael Plummer was here. The 22nd he was here too."

An early Los Angeles Bar.

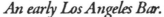

According to tradition, on one of Raf's visits to El Escorpion Espiritu saved him from the bite of a scorpion.

18

Mulligan Extorts the Wrong Man—Disposition of the Virgenes Case

Brunson pushed the case against the Virgines squatters, and it was speedily brought to trial. To their astonishment, the defendants discovered that they had no lawyer. They told the court they had employed Richard Mulligan, Esq., to defend their case. They said they had paid him a retainer and supposed that he was attending to their case, since he had agreed to do so.

When Mulligan was sent for, however, he appeared with a greatly elongated jaw and insisted to the judge that he had not been employed by the squatters. He stated that they had indeed come to his office and tried to employ him, offering him a two-hundred dollar retainer and a good fee besides, but that he had informed them he had such a relation to the litigant in this case that he could not professionally and ethically be employed by them. When they afterward still prevailed upon him to take their case, he had again informed them it would be impossible.

Whereupon, one of the squatters—the spokesman of the committee at the time the retainer was paid—stood up and told the judge that they had engaged Richard Mulligan and paid him the two hundred dollars.

Mulligan responded that he could refute that. There had been several gentlemen in his office who witnessed the discussion, he said, "Here is Mr. Kanacka and Mr. Biscailuz. They were present and know

169

that I refused the money. The truth is, if the defendants had any money at the time, they spent it—all of them went on a big drunk that day. Further, your honor, I think my professional standing ought to be sufficient to refute this base insinuation that I took these men's money and agreed to their employ. Why, sir, I could not stand in this court and look your honor in the face if I had done that. I could never be guilty of so base an act." And with that, Richard Mulligan, Esq., turned upon his heel and left the courtroom, followed closely by El Kanacka and Biscailuz.

The judge said the case would have to go on. The result was that a judgment was duly entered for the defendants' ejection. A case of action was issued, and the sheriff of Los Angeles County went to the Virgines and removed all of the squatters.

Time rolled along. Leonis had about recovered from the financial drafts made upon him from the numerous complications. He had begun to feel happy again, when he received a letter from Richard Mulligan, Esq.—it was a request for him to call at Mulligan's office. When Leonis presented himself there, he found Mulligan, El Kanacka, Biscailuz, and one or two other persons whom he did not know.

Biscailuz acted as an interpreter, since Leonis could not speak English.

"I have sent for you, Don Miguel," Mulligan began, "for I think it time for a settlement with you, for my services in that Virgines squatter case."

"I don't understand you, sir," responded Leonis.

"You don't understand me! You agreed to pay me for my services in assisting Brunson."

"Surely I never did. This is the first I hear of it. You told me once that you were assisting Brunson and that you looked to Brunson for your pay."

"I could not have told you such a thing, Don Miguel, because you and I had a special contract. You agreed to pay me twenty thousand dollars if I would assist Brunson, in case he was successful in the action."

"What do you mean by talking this way!" said Leonis, who was riling up.

"I mean that you shall pay me. I mean, sir, that this contract was made in the presence of Mr. Biscailuz and Mr. Kanacka, and I mean, sir, that you shall pay me!"

Eyes flashing, Leonis arose to his feet. He stood rigid for a moment, his teeth clenched and the muscles of his face working. Then he took up Mulligan in one hand and lifted El Kanacka in the other, and bumped them hard together thump, thump, thump—then dropped them helpless upon the floor. Next, he seized Biscailuz and thrashed him against the table until its boards shattered.

The others present rushed out the door and into the hall. Recovering himself with the utmost self-possession, Leonis also stepped into the hall. To the first gentleman he encountered, he said in the best English he could muster, "These men drunk. They too much fight."

Then he quietly walked down the stairs and went on his way to Mascarel's Tendajon de la Campana, where he informed him what had transpired.

"Nothing strange about that," remarked Mascarel. "That is the way of those thieving lawyers, and that boracho (drunk) Mulligan is the worst of the lot. I told you, Miguel, to have nothing with them."

I didn't—not until today. I guess I have had enough to do with them for the present."

"Wait," said Mascarel, "There is something that needs to be done in a hurry. You stay here. I will go," and Mascarel hurried off to the Justice's court. Asking his honor to step outside at the back door, Mascarel slipped a twenty-dollar gold piece into his hand and informed him what had happened at Mulligan's Poverty Club office. He then requested him to deny any warrant for Leonis' arrest in case the lawyers should make a complaint. This his honor readily promised, and Mascarel handed him another ten dollars for the constable.

Mulligan, Biscailuz and El Kanacka went into retirement for a time. It was weeks before they appeared at the usual places where they

171

were known so well. Rumors soon rumors spread that bones set and contusions doctored up—for sly Mascarel had told his friends what had happened.

When the three worthies appeared in town again, they were as silent as oysters. Mulligan looked as though his chin had been chopped off, and he walked with a cane—a great big, thick cane. Limping along with it one day, he met Haley.[1] "Hello Dick," Haley said. "Have you seen Leonis today?"

"What have I to do with Leonis, Haley? He is your man."

"Yes, but, Dick, I have it on the confidential that Leonis broke every bone in your body. Judging from the way you look, I am inclined to believe it. And what of Biscailuz? Have you seen him lately? To tell you the truth, Dick, Mascarel told me all about it. How you tried to claim twenty thousand dollars from Leonis for helping Brunson in the squatter case. And I remember, Dick, when you told me Leonis was after me about that squatter business. I congratulate myself, Richard Mulligan, Esq., that you are the man he lit upon and not me. Ah! Richard! Richard! my bones are whole. Come, Dick, and have a drink. You look dry as a fish."

The two walked from the courthouse steps over to Jake Philippi's, and whom should they meet there but Charles Granville Johnston, Esq., who said, "Hello, Dick. What's the matter? You don't look like the same man. You look as though you had been run through a thrashing machine, or a cyclone took you up and thrashed you down, or drove you through a brick wall. I declare, Dick, I never saw a man look so played out. Well, I believe I will join you. Yes, I will take whiskey, for mine."

"I will take whiskey, too," said Mulligan, and he gulped it down. "I guess I will take another," he said, and drank that, too. Then he took Haley aside, "Have you a spare dollar?"

"Why, yes, Dick—considering the situation, and the service you did me in turning Leonis away from me and upon yourself. Here's a dollar," Haley departed smiling, leaving the two leading lawyers to themselves.

Johnston turned to Mulligan, "How much did you get out of Haley? You know you owe me four bits, Dick."

"I don't owe you a cent. Say that again and I will mash you."

"I am tired of this, Dick. If you don't pay me that four bits I am going to take it out of your hide."

Mulligan did not feel very warlike, so he handed Haley's dollar to the barkeeper to get change and passed the four bits over. "Here, Johnston, I guess you will have to set 'em up for the next round."

"No, Dick, I guess you will have to set 'em up. Barkeeper, pass over the liquor. I want whiskey, and Mulligan wants whiskey." The two drank in silence.

"Now," said Johnston, "You plank down another four bits and pay for these drinks, or I will wipe up the floor with you." And, for the first time in history, Richard Mulligan, Esq., paid for the drinks.

Leonis had succeeded in ejecting the squatters, but soon other squatters took their places. By that time, however, Brunson had became a judge. He had received fourteen hundred acres of the Virgines as the contingent part of his fee in the squatter case. This he immediately transferred to an old Spanish lady, Senora Valdez, in exchange for a small but valuable tract of U.S.-patented land in the Cahuenga valley. This land he converted into money. It seems that Brunson himself did not have great confidence in the ultimate success of his plan.

But after a time Leonis brought a suit before Brunson. The case was called "Dominguez vs. Botiller" and can be found in the California Supreme Court Reports. This was an action to quiet title to the Virgines ranch—against the Botillers, the squatters and the United States of America.

It is not strange that Brunson rendered a decision in favor of his former client—standing by his opinion as rendered in that previous case. Again, the ruling was a bombshell, an act of judicial audacity unparalleled in the United States. And, strange to say, the Supreme Court of California, in the case above cited, affirmed Brunson's judgment. The reasoning was that the Dominguez had a good title from under the Mexican government, even though they did not lay it before the U.S. Land Commission, because the Treaty of Guadalupe Hidalgo was superior and paramount to the act of Congress that created the Land Commission.

Of course, the case was appealed to the Supreme Court of the United States—which reversed Brunson's ruling and the affirmation of it by the Supreme Court of the State of California. And so, the eight leagues of the Virgines ranch became relegated to the public domain—and the squatters got every acre of it.

It would be too unpleasant to recount here all the strife, bloodshed, murders, killings, and many lawless acts committed during the years of contest for possession of that beautiful part of Los Angeles County.

Leonis was badly cast down as a result of his long, continued and expensive litigation. He had been honest in his purchase of the land. He had been honest in his belief that he had a clear title. He had poured out coin like water in defense of his rights, and the money he intended to send to the Pyrenees was used up in this effort.

At this time, Leonis' estate consisted of seven thousand acres of land that he had purchased at the Laguna de Chico Lopez, the Escorpion, a great hotel at Santa Barbara,[2] an orchard residence in Los Angeles, and several blocks and houses in the commercial part of the city worth at least three quarters of a million. But these properties consisted his working capital. His intent had been to make the million dollars from the income, without sacrificing the principal.

Weary years had dragged along, but soon great encouragement came to him in the form of news from the Pyrenees. The leaven had worked—the Basque people were ripe for revolution. In a letter, Father Jean begged Miguel to return.

Endnotes

1. Very likely Salisbury Haley. The lawyers names you will find in this story were remarkably interconnected. There was a firm of Brunson, Eastman and Graves, then Brunson and Eastman, Brunson and Wells, later Salisbury Haley, John Robarts and an A. J. King. J. A. Graves, in *My Seventy Years In California*, describes the ruin of James G. Eastman as follows. Note how his description parallels some of Bell's narrative. Although Eastman does not appear in Bell's story, Haley, Brunson and Robarts all do.

    "Eastman formed a new connection with Salisbury Haley, John Robarts and A. J. King. Things went from bad to worse with him. Finally, his wife, in self-defense, had to leave him, taking their only daughter with her. He took up with a Spanish woman who had some means, and who was undoubtedly kind to him until she had to dismiss him. He became a tramp, wandering from saloon to saloon, where he could always obtain a drink without pay. Every day, for years, he would apply to me for fifty cents, and he always got it. I took him to Jacoby Brothers' store and brought him a complete new outfit, including underclothing, shoes, outer garments and an overcoat, at a cost of $110. He thanked me profusely, took the goods in two packages, and in two separate trips, to a second-hand dealer named Horatio Martine, and sold them for $11.

    He finally went to live at the county hospital. He would walk into town every day and back at night. He became a loathsome object to look upon, and died in absolute misery."

2. In fact, Leonis had a 50% interest. Jose Mascarel owned the other 50%.

Leonis

19

Jean Pierre Flees to Marseilles—Reveals Basque Conspiracy to Spanish Goverment Officials

Having secured five thousand francs from Mascarel on his letter of credit from Father Jean, the ex-friar Jean Pierre left Marseilles and made his way directly to the capital of Spain. Once in Madrid and still wearing friar's garb, he sought an interview with the head of the police department—stating that his business was of a secret and important character. He was promptly dispatched to the presence of the highest police functionary of the capital.

Before this official, the ex-friar laid the plan of the preparations for a revolution and of the setting up of a Basque republic within the Pyrenees. He told of Miguel Leonis, a man who years before had been notorious as a contraband king in the Basses Pyrenees[1] and was now in California, laying up immense wealth before his return to lead the revolution. He said that Father Jean of the monastery was the brains and arch schemer, and that all the leading male Basques on the French side of the line were committed to the cause. And that Leonis had recently visited the monastery and then mysteriously departed, presumably to California, and that upon his return the standard of revolution surely would be raised and the mountains become aflame with war. Jean Pierre even suggested that Spanish Basques would be dragooned into the revolution if they did not enter it willingly—also hinting that, so far as he understood, the revolution already had many adherrents on the Spanish side of the line.

He revealed that Leonis had brought five million francs with him from California, but that as to its disposition he could not say, although he understood it to consist of drafts on the Bank of France. He assured them that as soon as Leonis procured more money he would return.

Having presented this information and been interrogated minutely—answering intelligently and satisfactorily all of the questions asked of him—Jean Pierre was turned over to another officer. He was conducted to his lodging and placed under surveillance for the present, while the high official at once sought an interview with Spain's minister of justice.

Let us return now to Pierre Mascarel in Marseilles. The merchant had written to Father Jean to acknowledge the receipt of his letter and to inform him that he had honored his request to provide five thousand francs to Friar Jean Pierre. The reply that arrived swiftly from the father superior stated in no uncertain terms that Jean Pierre was no longer a friar at the monastery, that he had been degraded and expelled, and that the letter of credit he presented was clearly a forgery.

At the same time that he received Father Jean's expose, Mascarel was visited by the keeper of the cheap lodging place and canteen where the ex-friar had stayed. Hat in hand, the innkeeper told Mascarel that a friar had recently lodged at his house, where he became very drunk and early the next morning departed without settling his bill.

"We found these papers in his room. Seeing your name written upon them, I have brought them to you—thinking perhaps you have some connection with the friar and would settle his debt."

Glancing over the papers, Mascarel thanked the man for what he had done, offered to pay the bill of the false friar, and asked some questions of him—but elicited no information on the whereabouts of Jean Pierre. Mascarel paid the bill, gave the man a gratuity, and dismissed him.

Then he examined the papers. One was a letter of credit signed in Mascarel's name to Micheaux y Ca., bankers of Vera Cruz, Mexico, asking them to furnish Monsieur Jean Pierre with all the funds he might require, upon his presentation of this letter. Mascarel studied carefully this document that he had not written—it was a perfect imitation of his signature, he himself would not have been able to detect the falsity of it. Then he compared the text of the letter with the one brought by the ex-friar Jean Pierre from Father Jean, and found the writing to be exactly the same. Next, he picked up a letter of credit addressed to banker Estinou of Mexico City, extending an unlimited credit to Monsieur Jean Pierre. The third was a letter of recommendation to the Larronde brothers in the city of Leon, introducing the bearer, Monsieur Jean Pierre, and requesting kind assistance and service for him—representing that he was visiting the republic of Mexico on private and important business for the writer, Mr. Mascarel of Marseilles. These last two letters were in all particulars as perfect as the first. Finally, there were some sheets of paper upon which the ex-friar had practiced writing signatures. Signature after signature he had written as though for the purpose of comparison with the genuine signatures he evidently was trying to forge.

Mascarel was dumbfounded, absolutely paralyzed, and for a time all he could do was ponder over the subject. Then he at once wrote to all his Mexican correspondents, the ones named in Jean Pierre's papers and others, in other towns and places, stating the matter of his discovery and requesting them to be on their guard against imposition.

Jean Pierre clearly intended to go to Mexico, but in the event he might proceed from there to California, Mascarel wrote to his brother in Los Angeles to warn him. Having done all this, he took the train to Bayonne. From there, he continued to Cambo and visited Father Jean at the monastery.

That evening Father Jean remarked to his visitor, "These recent forgeries explain to me similar things that were once inexplicable. Orders of mine, written on tradesmen of the town for small things, frequently came in and were audited by my secretary, Friar Jean Pierre, and, along with all the other bills coming against the monastery, were duly honored. But there were orders I could not account for—although in my writing and bearing my signature—and I began to fear that my memory was failing me. I was perplexed. I had no memory of writing such orders but, still, there was my writing, there was my signature—better evidence than my memory!—only now is it all explained. Only now do I realize, I had a secretary who could write my name and counterfeit my signature so well that I could not detect it myself. I never suspected, my good friend Mascarel, until your letter came, that I had been the victim of a most arrant scoundrel and expert forger. But what are we to do? Prudent foresight is futile protection against the lies of the perjurer, the knife of the assassin, or the perfect pen of the forger."

They were still in conversation when Monsieur Ballade, innkeeper from the village, came in—carrying an order from Father Jean by the hand of the ex-friar Jean Pierre, for the sum of one hundred francs. Father Jean looked at Mascarel and Mascarel stared at Father Jean. Ballade stood in a confused manner because he had never met with such a strange reception at the hands of the good Father Jean, who was the epitome of politeness and human kindness.

Father Jean broke the silence, "My good friend Ballade, I am engaged in a very important and precarious matter of business, so if you will excuse me for the present and call me tomorrow, we will make a settlement."

Ballade, hat in hand, retired from the room.

"There it is," said Father Jean to Mascarel. "This is the beginning, but where will it end? What shall I do about this one hundred francs? It is not much, perhaps the only one in the village, because upon his expulsion from the monastery, Jean Pierre apparently went to the tavern—carrying with him this order, or concocting it while there. Ballade seems honest in his premises. I think I will take my chances, when he returns on the morrow I will pay the hundred francs. If that is the last of it here in Cambo, I will be satisfied."

Mascarel had accepted the hospitality of the monastery for the day and the night. On the following morning he was conducted to the railroad station, where he took a train to Bayonne and from there continued to Marseilles.

The ex-friar Jean Pierre meanwhile stood in the presence of the Minister of Justice and was introduced to another official, El Senor Muyoscuro,[2] chief of the foreign division of Spain's secret service.

"Having engaged yourself in this business, Senor Jean Pierre, you will accompany this gentleman to California. He has his instructions fully written out and will obey them to the letter. You will be his assistant, you will act under his directions and obey him implicitly. I have ordered my secretary to pay you a stated sum, which I believe we have agreed upon, and upon the accomplishment of your joint mission to California, you will be paid the other stated sum we agreed upon. I feel that I can trust you, and I have confidence in your fidelity because of the presence at your side of my trusted agent, El Senor Muyoscuro. You will depart tomorrow for New York."

"Yes," answered the ex-friar, "but I have some important private business that calls me first to the capital of Mexico, and I may be detained in that republic for a month, not exceeding that time. It is a matter of great financial import to me and I beg permission to go to Vera Cruz, thence to Los Angeles, in California, where El Senor Muyoscuro can await for a few days in case he arrives sooner than I do. But he might prefer to accompany me by the way of the Mexican capital."

"What assurance have I that you will be faithful to your employ and go to Los Angeles at all? You might remain in Mexico."

"I think, considering the situation and the information I have given to the Spanish government—and the small stipend that is to pay my expenses to California, with the very high reward that I am to receive upon my return—this should be sufficient guarantee of my faithful performance of my part of the contract."

"I will expect you to call upon the Spanish consul at Vera Cruz," said the Minister, "and to present yourself at our legation at Mexico City. I will notify those dignitaries accordingly."

"I suppose that while in Mexico I will be placed under Spanish surveillance?"

"No, not that exactly," answered the Minister, "but still I want them to know that you are in the secret service of Spain."

"I think," chipped in El Senor Muyosuro, "that Senor Jean Pierre and I can travel together until we get to the point of the great railroad called El Paso Del Norte of Juarez, and then it is only a short distance down to Mexico City. I would like to go there with him. If he should be delayed in that city, I can turn about and continue my journey to Los Angeles. I have been over those railroads from New York often. I could almost repeat their time table from memory. I have never been to California. It will afford me much pleasure to visit that great country, which once formed part of our illustrious kingdom."

"You have your instructions, Senor," said the Minister, "I will depend upon you. You and Senor Jean Pierre may travel as you see fit."

The Minister rang a small bell. An underofficial appeared, who was ordered to conduct the two gentlemen to the financial secretary. The Minister then waved his hand in dismissal, and the two secret-service agents, hats in hand, bowed profoundly as they backed themselves away from his august presence.༝

Endnotes

1. Basses Pyrenees is no longer known by this name. In 1970 the Basque provinces of France were incorporated, along with Bearn, into the Department of the Pyrenees Atlantiques.

2. "Muyoscuro" is an amusing example of a name invented by Horace Bell for a character, fictitious, but required by the story. It can be loosely translated as "very obscure," or "very secret," an excellent trait for a spy.

A name like this signals the reader that this character is fictional, as distinct from the actual persons described.

In chapter 21 will be found Senor "Saldanyseguro," loosely translated as "One who repays his debts, for sure," a prophetic name, as you will discover.

Another similar name is "Mascarbo," but its meaning is not clear.

Leonis

20

Jean Pierre Goes to Mexico with Secret Agent Muyoscuro—Arrival in Los Angeles

Not long thereafter, the Mexican city of Vera Cruz was honored by the lofty presence of the ex-friar Jean Pierre. With a supercilious air, he presented himself at the banking house of Micheaux, and asked for the secretary. He was shown into the private office of the bank secretary, whereupon, with a profound bow, Jean Pierre presented his letter of credit from Pierre Mascarel.

"Ah!" said the secretary. "Monsieur, I am delighted to see you. I am glad to hear from our honored correspondent, Monsieur Mascarel. He is the soul of honor. If he lives long enough, he will surely become the leading merchant of the world."

"Yes, Senor," answered Jean Pierre, "Mascarel is a great man. I am proud to list him among my patrons and friends. My father and his father were friends, and I am glad to list him as the best friend I have in the world."

The secretary opened his desk and removed a document from a pigeon hole. This he opened and compared with the letter of credit presented to him by Jean Pierre.

"I received this letter of credit in advance," the secretary said. "You will see it is the same writing—the same signature, the same date—and I have here a letter from Pierre Mascarel himself, informing me that it is a forgery, and that if you were to present this to us at this bank, with any letter from him, letter of credit, or recommendation or otherwise, we are to know it is a forgery. He advises us that you are an arrant scoundrel and a most dangerous man, a most expert forger. And now, my dear sir, how long do you propose to remain in Mexico? In ten days from today I shall advise the police of your presence. If you are still here in Vera Cruz, it will go hard with you. I will retain both of these documents. If you depart immediately, you will not be molested—but ten days from today the police will have the information. You may depart, sir."

The crestfallen ex-friar, his smile faded and grimace of supercilious confidence gone, slunk out of the room and left the bank.

"Of course," he thought later, when he had composed himself enough to ponder the situation, "Pierre Estinou of Mexico City must also have been advised. I see now how it is. When I was at that canteen and drank too much of that wretched wine, I lost the first of those letters I had written. They must have fallen into the hands of Mascarel, and so he has advised all his correspondents in Mexico. Very well, I will not stop in Mexico City to see Estinou. Instead, I will hurry to Leon. Perhaps I may make a raise out of the Larronde brothers, and then ho! for California!"

Without loss of time, the ex-friar presented himself at the counting room of the Larronde brothers in Leon. To them, he presented a friendly letter of introduction from Monsieur Mascarel of Marseilles requesting the polite assistance and such other acts of kindness that the gentlemen might bestow upon "my particular friend—(giving a fictitious name)—as he might need while visiting Mexico." The letter continued: "He is in Leon on most important financial business and your advice may serve him, if nothing else. But be kind to him for my sake."

"What can I do for you?" asked Monsieur Larronde. "I am absolutely at your service, Monsieur."

"Why, you could give me a letter of introduction to some person in Mexico City, merely that I may know someone there, someone who may introduce me to parties with whom I will have business."

"Certainly," answered Larronde. "Pierre Estinou, a prominent banker, is my particular friend and I will introduce you to him."

Thereupon, Larronde wrote a letter of introduction and signed his name. He invited the ex-friar to dine with him, but the invitation was declined on the ground that Jean Pierre had to be in Mexico City at the earliest possible hour. Then, with a great amount of politeness and suave condescension, the ex-friar took his departure.

Upon his arrival in the capital, Jean Pierre immediately presented himself at the bank of Pierre Estinou, where he was received kindly. The question was asked, "What service can we be to you, Monsieur?"

"The truth is," said Jean Pierre, "I am here on some business that I must despatch within the next fortnight, but I am short of funds. If you can let me have a few dollars, I will consider it a great favor."

So the bank lent him $600 and on the same day he was whirling over the Mexican Central for El Paso, in the state of Texas, and then on to California. Settled down in the smoking car, the ex-Friar ruminated over and over how well he had done. He thrust his two bowed legs over a chair in front of him and chuckled.

We next find him in Los Angeles, at the Pyrenees Hotel on Alameda Street, which was kept by one Ballade, perhaps a brother or a cousin of his friend Ballade in the village of Cambo. So thought the ex-friar but he did not say anything to this Ballade of Los Angeles. He informed the innkeeper that he was a priest—one recommended to Bishop Mora, the bishop of Monterey and Los Angeles—but that he desired to remain in the hotel quietly and incognito. Ballade was instructed that his guest did not want it generally known who he was or what was his object in visiting Los Angeles. Jean Pierre explained that he was a student as well as a priest, and he only desired to become aquainted with the learned people of the town—scholars, priests, judges, lawyers and others of the upper crust.

The day after his arrival, Jean Pierre was called on by Senor Muyoscuro and the two had an interesting private conversation, after giving particular attention to the security of all doors and windows.

"I realized the walls have ears and we are in the secret service of Spain," Jean Pierre began. "We are here to nip a great revolution in the bud. The self-exiled Hannibal, Miguel Leonis, must be compelled to remain in California, and now we must devise a plan for how it shall be done. Whose acquaintance have you made here that might assist us?"

"It was a short run you made to Vera Cruz, Senor Jean Pierre. I didn't expect you for another two weeks, so I have not sought the acquaintance of anyone in particular—only the acting Spanish consul and two or three residents who are Spaniards but not naturalized Americans. How I do detest the Spanish American. A Spaniard ought to be a Spaniard and nothing else. Those who come to this country and forswear allegiance to Spain, I wouldn't trust beyond the reach of a dagger. They are no good. I want to find out how many Spaniards—true Spaniards—we have here, and then I will lay plans."

"I have, however, seen Leonis," Muyoscuro continued. "I went to the store on the upper corner of the Plaza, the one kept by Mascarel. That is Leonis' headquarters when he comes to town. I lounged around there, spent a little money among the loafers who came in, played cards a time or two, even talked with Mascarel. I tell you, this Mascarel is no fool. He is the slyest and sharpest old coon I have ever met. When I stand in the presence of this Mascarel, somehow or other I feel small—not because I am a man small in stature and he a physical giant, but because I sense the man has a master mind. All the time I was there I felt that he was reading me. We must be careful of this Mascarel. Of course, I had to go there because I was laying for Leonis. I wanted to size up the contraband king for myself."

"I know something of this Mascarel," said Jean Pierre. "I am going to present a letter of introduction from his merchant brother of Marseilles, whom I have the honor to know. Particular friend of mine, the Marseilles man."

"You have a letter from him to his brother?"

"Not yet, but I will write one soon."

"Surely you do not expect to impose upon this man with a pretended letter from his brother, written by yourself?!"

"Yes, of course I do—and it will be a letter which for his life he could not say that it was not written by his brother."

With that, Jean Pierre produced some genuine letters from Pierre Mascarel to Father Jean of the Cambo Monastery and some letters forged by him—and the secret-service gentleman could not tell which was which. Muyoscuro stood in utter amazement.

Soon the two strolled out to take in the town. On Main Street opposite Commercial, they met an elegantly dressed, fine-looking gentleman to whom they spoke and inquired as to which was the best restaurant in town. The gentleman responded politely to them and handed his card.

"Mr. Emil Roth, at your service, gentlemen. With your permission, seeing that you are strangers, I will accompany you to the establishment of Monsieur Dol, who keeps a restaurant equal to the best in Paris."[1]

So the two secret-service gentlemen of the Spanish government and Mr. Emil Roth, who was a French American, entered a private room of the great restaurant of Mr. Dol.

"Now," said Senor Muyoscuro, "Monsieur Roth, do us the honor to sit down with us and recommend the best wines of this country. I have heard it said that they are to be exalted—supposedly they surpass the best vintages of France, Spain and Italy—and I want to test them."ↄ

Endnotes

1. In *History and Reminiscences: Los Angeles City and County*, William A. Spalding recalled Victor Dol's restaurant: "Midway of the (Downey) block on Main Street a hallway led through to an inner court with a fountain, and in ample rooms around it, Victor Dol established, in the late '70s, a French restaurant that took the shine out of the Delmonico."

Leonis

21

Miguel's Note Forged—Bell Hired for Lawsuit Against Saldanyoseguro—Jean Pierre Jailed

After leaving the restaurant and taking leave of Monsieur Roth, the secret-service agent of Spain abruptly confronted Jean Pierre, "Senor, I am afraid of you and intend to lay down the law for the future. You drink too much wine and you talk too much. You are what we call in Spanish 'muy lenguaz (garrulous).' I will accompany you to your room, as I don't wish to talk like this on the street." It was now seven or eight o'clock in the evening, and many people were passing and repassing on Main and Commercial streets.

Arriving at Jean Pierre's room in the Hotel Pyrenees, taking care to close the doors, Muyoscuro opened his full batteries upon the ex-friar: "I don't know who this Monsieur Roth is, and you don't know any more about him than I do. He is a French Jew and as loquacious as yourself. It would have been all right for us to have drawn him out so as to find out what we could in respect to Leonis. But you, fool that you are—and remember, sir, you are responsible to me for your conduct here, just as I am responsible to his excellency, the Minister of Justice in Madrid—I say, fool that you are, you almost gave us away and the object of our coming here! What made you tell Monsieur Roth that Leonis is your uncle? If I had you in Madrid, or any other place in Spain, I would put esposas (handcuffs) on you and tumble you into the first lockup! And I would keep you there! And I would see that you didn't get any wine! This Monsieur Roth was sizing us up and now he knows what we came here for. I wish you were at the bottom of the sea and that I were free of you! Hereafter, keep yourself to yourself! Stay off the streets—keep out of company. When I want you, I will let you know! Adios, majadero, (numbskull)!" and, with that, the disdainful Spaniard turned his back and left the room, slamming the door behind him.

Left to himself, the ex-friar went downstairs to the barroom and purchased a bottle of red wine commonly called "sheep-herder's delight," which he caressed as he carried it to his room. He sat down at a table with the bottle before him, alternately taking a drink and talking to himself, "Ha! If he had me in Spain it would be handcuffs and a darkened cell! Well, thank the Lord I am not in Spain. Nor am I in France, but here, in free America, in the 'garden spot of California.' The world is a vineyard and I a lover of grapes—so I propose to help myself. Numbskull, he called me. Well, I suppose I have already got from the Spanish government as much as I will ever get. I would like to make some money here. I need money, and either out of Mascarel or Leonis I will get it! I am afraid of both of them, but still, I must have some money."

From under the head of his bed, Jean Pierre drew a satchel and took from it packages of papers and letters—including some from Leonis in California to Father Jean at Cambo. He sat down at the table with them, unfolded letter after letter and lay them all down before him. Then, returning all but one to the satchel, which he pushed aside, he took from the drawer of the little table several sheets of writing paper, pen and ink. He went to work copying one of Leonis' letters, with special attention to the signature. Then he compared the copy with the original and took a separate sheet of paper, where he wrote 'Leonis' over and over again, imitating each stroke with care.

"The signature is perfect," he said aloud. "My copy is perfect. Leonis always writes his name in the same manner—this would indicate a very straightforward man. Many men write their names one way today and a slightly different way tomorrow, so that when you compare all the various signatures there are no two exactly alike. Those of Leonis are always alike, however. He must be a very square man. That is my test of a man's honesty—an honest man always writes his name in the same manner, and so I will write 'Leonis' the same way."

Jean Pierre went over his various forgeries of Leonis' signatures, comparing each with the originals. Then he took from his pocket some printed promissory notes in blank. He wrote $4000 on the upper left-hand corner, in its proper place; then he wrote "on the — day of —, I promise to pay to the order of (himself) four thousand dollars" with interest, etc., until he filled up the blank in its entirety. Signing Leonis' name, he then carefully read over the note and again compared it with all the other signatures.

"Well done," he congratulated himself, "I couldn't do it better if I had written a hundred. This will do for the present. I could have made it for ten thousand dollars as well as four thousand, but I will take my chances on this as an experiment. I have heard that Leonis' notes are good for twenty thousand dollars in any of the banks. When he comes to take up this note, he will never suspect that he didn't make it himself. If it were for ten thousand he might hesitate to pay it, but four thousand—I think it will stick."

Folding the note carefully, Jean Pierre placed it in his pocketbook and returned the pocketbook to its place in the inside of his coat. He folded up the letters and replaced them in the satchel, after which he emptied the bottle of "sheepherder's delight" and went to bed.

Leonis had not been in Los Angeles for a long time. He was reorganizing the operations of his ranchos, which by this time were all in prosperous condition—stocked with fatted cattle, well-broken horses, mules for farming purposes, machinery for wheat growing, hay presses, wine vats and everything pertaining to stock raising and agriculture on a grand scale.

The losses and mishaps that had befallen him during his absence, and the money spent in the squatter litigation, were now forgotten, and all of his affairs were moving along like clockwork. He had built an imposing house at Calabasas—planted a vineyard and an orchard, fenced in acres with the most substantial and improved method of post-and-plank fencing, built windmills and water tanks; and there were trading posts and taverns removed some distance from the house. This manorial mansion he had given to Espiritu, his faithful housekeeper, with the twenty thousand dollars kept on deposit for her use should he die or return home to the Pyrenees.[1]

It so happened that about a month after the arrival in Los Angeles of Senor Muyoscuro and the ex-friar Jean Pierre, Leonis paid Mascarel a visit—one that had more of a friendly and fraternal character than of business, because herewith Miguel conveyed by deed to Mascarel, all duly recorded, the entirety of his vast estate. Mascarel had advanced Miguel the money he needed to make up the deficit in the million dollars he had pledged himself to raise, for the revolutionary fund in Cambo. The Big Basque was making his preparations to leave California and had about completed them, of which no one had knowledge except for Mascarel.

On this visit Miguel informed Mascarel that before he went away he intended to file one last lawsuit. A certain Senor Saldanyoseguro had stirred up considerable mischief for Leonis during his absence. In Miguel's opinion, the man had molested, harassed, and annoyed him in every manner conceivable.

"And he owes me," said Leonis, "a total of more than two thousand dollars—which I had lent him from time to time. I would no longer bother to try to collect except for his malicious and contemptible conduct. The man has persisted in smiting the hand that fed him, and I propose to do him up before I leave California."

The wise Mascarel advised against this, "This is too small a matter for you, Miguel, and it may interfere with your departure. Leave the account with me and perhaps I can collect it sometime."

"No," said Leonis, "I intend to bring suit against him, and I propose to attach his horses, his mules and his burros. In all justice they are mine, anyway. I have endured so much insolence from this fellow that I want to be here to witness the humiliation that I propose to bring upon him. Before I leave Los Angeles, I want to hire a lawyer and authorize him to proceed."

"I am convinced," Miguel continued, "that this scoundrel Saldanyoseguro was once hired to assassinate me, and I will relate the particulars if you think they will interest you. One night I was called to my door, and when I stood in the full light of a lamp, which was burning behind me, I was shot at—the bullet perforating my clothing and lodging itself in the wall opposite and behind me. I got a glimpse of the scoundrel as he ran away, so I ran after him. In the darkness he plunged into the willow copse in the bottom opposite my house and escaped, but I was satisfied at the time that it was Saldanyoseguro. I did not tell you of this before—nor have I told you of other attempts to kill me, as I journeyed from ranch to ranch attending to my affairs—because, my good friend, I did not wish to alarm you for my safety. Much as I would like to, I cannot hang the ruffian. I cannot send him to prison, because I do not have sufficient evidence against him. But I can hurt him worse, by depriving him of his livestock, and I propose to do it. After it is done, I will tell him why I did it."

"Which lawyer do you want to use?"

"I want the lawyer Bell."[2]

"Bell?! Why, he has fought you in the courts these twenty years. You have paid wheelbarrow loads of money on lawsuits conducted by Bell against you. Why should you want him?"

"Well, it is true he has fought against me in the courts, and he usually prevailed in his suits against me—but I believe him to be honest. He always treated me fairly; he stood opposite me, face to face. After thinking over the matter, I have come to the conclusion that Bell is an honest man. I intend to have him on my suit, if I can get him."

"Very well," said Mascarel, "but I still strongly advise against this action."

The suit was brought on the following day. The ranch stock of the defendant was duly attached and taken in charge by an officer.

Leonis rested. He remained in town for nearly a week, he and Mascarel having a good social time. They were very fond of each other, with a friendship and devotion as true as that of Damon to Pythias and Pythias to Damon.

One morning, Mascarel and Leonis were at breakfast at the Dol restaurant in Downey block when a messenger arrived from the bank, with a request for them to call on Mr. Hellman. After finishing their meal, the two walked over to the bank—where Hellman exhibited the four-thousand-dollar note so deftly forged by the ex-friar Jean Pierre. Hellman handed the note to Leonis and asked when he would pay it. Dumbfounded, Leonis passed it to Mascarel.

Mascarel scanned it very carefully and after much scrutiny he said, "In the devil's name, Miguel, what does this mean? All this time, you have kept large sums of money in my hands and in this bank, and then you give out a note for four thousand dollars? Why did you do it?"

"I never signed this note," said Leonis.

"But it is your signature," persisted Mascarel, passing the note to Hellman.

"Yes, it is your signature," Hellman agreed.

The banker asked Leonis to step aside to a desk and write his name. This Leonis did. Then, at Hellman's request, he wrote it several times more, with different pens and different kinds of ink, and—when the signatures were compared with the one appearing on the four-thousand-dollar note, they were found to look exactly the same.

The note had been endorsed to Mr. Roth.

"Did Roth bring this note here?" Mascarel inquired of Hellman.

"Yes, he left it here for collection, and what is worse he borrowed two thousand dollars on it. Had I been here it would have been different because, notwithstanding the signature, I would have had my suspicions. The note is made payable to Monsieur Goytino—but who is he?"

Mascarel turned to Leonis, "Are you willing to swear that you never made this note?"

"Of course I am—and I intend to have this Goytino arrested, whoever he may be. But before we proceed, let us send for Mr. Roth and see what he has to say about it."

A bank messenger was sent at once to the office of Mr. Roth, who was a broker, and in a few minutes Roth presented himself at the bank. Closeted in a back room with Hellman, Mascarel and Leonis, Roth explained that he had been acquainted only a few days with Goytino, who seemed a very plausible and respectable gentleman.

"He introduced himself to me as a nephew of Senor Leonis, recently arrived from France. He said he had come to act as secretary and assistant manager for Leonis in

According to this story Mr. Goytino was originally the ex-friar John Peter, of the Cambo Monastery. Mr. Goytino is buried at the Calvary Cemetery, in East Los Angeles.

his great estates and business, and that he resided with his uncle at El Escorpion. He also told me he had brought with him considerable money, which as an accommodation, he had lent to Leonis in exchange for a note for four thousand dollars. I understood him to say that he had large financial interests in Mexico and quite recently had accommodated a French naval officer here with a loan, so that now he was a little short of money. Not wishing to let Leonis know of his financial condition, he offered to sell me the note. I purchased it, took his endorsement and here it is. I thought the better place to leave it would be this bank. Of course the note is good and Mr. Leonis will pay it, when it suits his pleasure. I have had two thousand dollars advance on the note and I am willing to wait on Mr. Leonis' convenience in getting the remainder. I did not ask, Mr. Hellman, that Mr. Leonis should be notified to come and pay the note—so I did not expect to find him here making inquiries about it. That is all I can say, gentlemen, therefore I will bid you good day."

"But where is Mr. Goytino, whoever he may be?" asked Mascarel.

"I don't know," answered Roth, "I assume he is at the Escorpion or Calabasas or at the Laguna, looking out for Mr. Leonis' interests. I understood that to be his business, and I suppose Mr. Leonis can tell you more about that than I can. Therefore, gentlemen, I must bid you good day," And with that Roth departed.

Inside of an hour a warrant was placed in the hands of an officer for the arrest of Jean Pierre Goytino, on a charge of forgery, the complaint being sworn to by Miguel Leonis. The next morning, Mascarel and Leonis were notified that Goytino had been safely locked up in a cell at the county bastile.[3]

After breakfast the two went to the bank, where Mr. Hellman joined them, and the three proceeded to the county jail for an interview with the prisoner. In a brief space of time, the prisoner was brought into the corridor of the great prison—and lo! Leonis was confronted with the sight of Jean Pierre, ex-friar and former secretary at the monastery at Cambo.

Leonis' astonishment was such that he could not speak, and all he could do was stare—at those same bullet eyes, the same bald head and supercilious smile, the same cunning expression, the distinctive knock knees and clumsy turkey-foot thrust in Jean Pierre's wallowing gait.

Without embarassment or visible emotion, the prisoner wallowed up to Leonis with the warmest expressions of his happiness at their meeting. He seemed not the least bit abashed or ashamed of his situation, and when Hellman produced the note to confront him with it, with supreme effrontery, Jean Pierre responded: "Yes, that is Mr. Leonis' note. What about it?"

Miguel's eyes flashed as his body stiffened—his teeth set, the muscles of his face twitching, and his hands clenched until they looked like balls of iron.

Sensing what might follow, Mascarel immediately stepped in front of Leonis and said, "No! No! No! Not here. This scoundrel is under the protection of the sheriff of this county, it would be an act of disrespect to the authorities."

Leonis turned to Hellman and said just one word, "Vamonos" (let's go).

The turnkey sprang the lock and the three visitors departed from the prison.[4] ☙

Endnotes

1. Leonis did not "build" a house at Calabasas, but he did expand an exisiting adobe ranch house into a more elegant and comfortable home. Today we might look on "manorial mansion" as an amusing Bell exageration, but in its day it was an imposing residence, for Southern California. There is no evidence that Leonis ever intended to give Espiritu the house in Calabasas or twenty thousand dollars in cash. In his will, he left his "faithful housekeeper" ten thousand dollars—five thousand in cash and five thousand in trust.

   On May 20, 1891, a *Los Angeles Times* court reporter related the testimony of the lawyer John Robarts in regard to Leonis will: "Espiritu was in the office at the time the will was being drawn and objected to his provision that she should only receive $5000 in cash and $5000 in trust, saying she had been his helpmeet through life and she ought to have a common share of his property. Leonis objected, and told Mr. Robarts that if he gave her any more she would only let her son [by Menendez] spend it and throw it away. He said Espiritu had been more than a wife, that she had been his slave, and he wanted to see her provided for. (p.2)

Upon Miguel's death, Espiritu sued to break the will, on the ground that she had been living with Miguel Leonis in a common-law marriage lasting some 30 years. She ultimately prevailed, and the court recognized her as Leonis' wife.

2. This is Horace Bell. After years of seeing Bell represent people in court against him, Miguel Leonis eventually hired him.

3. On June 5, 1889, this item appeared in the *Los Angeles Express,* "Miguel Leonis, the millionaire, is confined at the French hospital, this city. From the moment J.P. Goytino was bound over by Justice Savage to answer before the Superior Court on a charge of forging Leonis' name, the millionaire became suddenly ill and his mind is said to be unbalanced. In his delirium Leonis calls for Goytino, who is his relative."

4. The *California Historical Society's* "The French Press in California" quotes the editor of a French periodical named *Le Gaulois,* a man named Raskin, for this assessment of Goytino's character—which appeared in the editor's 1891 farewell message, to his readers. He (Goytino) is decried as a wretched and miserable vagabond, former prisoner of the county of Los Angeles, who left France after three years in a congregation of monks when he was found guilty of a series of "crimes against nature." Forced to leave France because of his misdeeds and also because of his swindles to the detriment of his uncle Bernard Etcheverry, Goytino became stranded in California. "Everybody knows" he had something to do with the accidental death of his cousin Leonis, for which he should be occupying a cell in the state prison at San Quentin. He fortuitously became the editor of *Le Progres.* "Our readers know what he has done." (p.337)

Here are Raskin's exact words, "Un malheureux et misérable vagabond nommons-le, J-P. Goytino, ci-devant pensionnaire de la prison du comté de Los Angeles, a particulièrement pris à tâche de nous vilipender. Nous savons pertinemment qu'il a appartenu en France, pendant trois ans, à la congrégation des Frères ignorantins, sous le nom de Frère Lupulus, et qu'il s'y est rendu coupable d'une série de crimes contre nature. Forcé de quitter la France par suite des ces méfaits—et aussi par suite des actes d'escroquerie et de faux commis au préjudice de son oncle, M. Bernard Etcheverry, il a échoué en Californie. Tout le monde sait qu'il ne doit qu'à la mort accidentelle de son cousin Léonis, de ne pas occuper aujourd'hui une cellule dans la prison d'Etat à San Quentin. C'est par suite de sa mise en liberté tout fortuite qu'il est devenu éditeur de *Progrès!* Nos lecteurs savent ce qu'il y a accompli." (also p. 337)

According to the California Historical Society account, "From contemporary records (Jean-Pierre Goytino) seems to have been an outstanding example of the worst traits of the Basques, but in spite of his very unsavory record in two countries, he was much feared and was rumored to have powerful connections . . . (H)e forged and passed a note of $3,800 in the name of his cousin Leonis, actually a cousin of his mother and called by him "Uncle" . . . Besides this, Goytino was reputed to have protected Basque murderers on several occasions and helped them to escape in return for cash. In 1894 he retired from *Le Progres* to apply himself to his 'etude de notair' and his Basque journal *Eskual-Herria* . . . A few years later Mme Trebaol objected to the appointment of Goytino as guardian of her minor brother (whose mother could not qualify because she did not speak English), and Goytino's wife, who was Mascarel's daughter and half-Indian, tried to whip her in the county court house, but failed to do any damage. When arrested for assault and battery she proved that she had paid her fine for it in advance. A curious way of administering the law, and as late as 1899! Nothing is definitely known about the date or manner of Goytino's death. It was rumored that he committed suicide when about to be criminally prosecuted in the federal courts." (pp.336-337)

Leonis

22

Secret Agent Visits Saldanyoseguro

Saldanyoseguro was a man of fearsome knowledge—crafty, daring, and unscrupulous. He had trained under the immediate command of the bandit revolutionist Lozada, of the Mexican state of Colima. When Lozada had been conquered, captured, and shot, and his so-called armies dispersed, the senor in question found the country too hot for him. He came to Los Angeles—a haven for rest and refuge, and a place of quietude to Mexican political outlaws as well as to general outlaws against social order.

When an officer armed with process appeared at his ranch in the Virgines mountains and levied a writ of attachment on his livestock—and then drove them to Los Angeles—Saldanyoseguro fumed. He boiled over. He was absolutely beside himself with rage. He vituperated Leonis and swore that he would be avenged upon him. He vowed he would lay him low, "boca a la tierra" (be made to bite the dust).

He followed the herds all the way to Los Angeles, making many efforts on the way to recapture them. But the officer had nerve and kept the senor at bay while his associates leisurely drove the stock.

This occurred a few days before the incarceration of the ex-friar Jean Pierre in the county jail. The stock was brought into the city and safely corraled. All that Saldanyoseguro could do was to employ a lawyer and fight it out in the courts as best he could. Two weeks later, the case went to trial and Leonis prevailed. He recovered judgment, and the stock was sold under the hammer by order of the court. It did not quite meet the amount specified in the judgment.

Leonis was much elated by his success in the suit. In recent years he had been so often beaten, mulcted in damages, and done up by lawyers, and had paid so many thousands of dollars in useless suits, that the outcome of this case reconciled him to his old legal enemy, the lawyer Bell. He instructed Mascarel that for whatever business he might have in the courts after Leonis' departure, Bell should be employed as his attorney.

On the day following the sale of Saldanyoseguro's stock, Leonis returned to the Escorpion and Calabasas to make final arrangements for his departure to the Pyrenees.

Saldanyoseguro's resentment toward Leonis was wild and ferocious. He vented all manner of anathemas upon him and returned to his ranch in the mountains crestfallen, sullen, and determined in his own mind as he laid plans for the successful assassination of Leonis.

"How shall I do this?" he thought. "Leonis is like a cat with many lives. It seems that even a bullet will not kill him. I have shot at him from face to face, and within ten feet of my rifle muzzle, and then I had to run away like a skulking coyote to escape his clutches. Once, I fired at him from the roadside, and again from the house where I was resting when he drove by in his buggy. It seemed to me that he didn't even hear the report of my gun, or the whizzing of the bullet, for he paid no attention whatever to any of those shots—except for the one at his house that night. I think I have fired six or seven times at Leonis. I need to try some different tactics. My old friend Lozada advocated the use of the dagger for such work, but should I use a dagger on Leonis I might not be able to kill him at the first stab—then with his great strength and vitality he would surely kill me."

While he was in this mood and ruminating on his situation, a rather elegant-looking gentleman, driving a good horse attached to a livery buggy, drove up to Saldanyoseguro's house and asked for a drink of water. He spoke the Spanish language so fluently, he was evidently a

Spaniard of the most intelligent and refined class. Saldanyoseguro asked him if he would not alight, refresh himself and rest, as it was near noontime and the day was quite hot.

"Your horse needs rest and refreshment also. I am poor but still I have enough in my house to entertain a visitor. And I have barley and hay, thank the Lord. Yes, I have barley and hay, but no horses to feed them to. Ah! Senor! Senor! Unfortunate am I, for I have been robbed, literally cleaned out."

In the meantime the visitor alighted from the buggy, and his host was soon at work taking the horse out of the shafts and removing the harness. An old Indian woman—a relic of a by-gone race—came out with a gourd full of water, from which the visitor drank with a great deal of gusto. Once the horse was disposed of and made comfortable, the host and his visitor seated themselves in the cool of the house corridor and entered into conversation.

Said the visitor, "My good friend, that man Leonis must be a tyrant—an overbearing, domineering, ruthless tyrant, whom any man would be justified in killing. He is not fit to live upon and curse this beautiful green earth, if what you are telling me is the truth."

"Yes, this is true," said Saldanyoseguro, "and someone will eventually kill him. That he has not been killed during all these years must certainly have been on account of protection from the devil. In fact, I do believe Leonis is the devil himself. Someone will kill him—and soon—of this you may be sure. Do you know him, Senor?"

"No, I have not met him, but I have heard his name spoken with disparagement by other persons in the neighborhood. I am visiting this region with a view to buying a ranch. I have plenty of money—I have just arrived from Europe and intend to settle down here in California. I would like to make friends with you. Your appearance suits me, I can see from your manner that you have been a soldier, Senor. I can tell from your style, your address. I have been a soldier, too."

"Yes, I have been a soldier. I served under that great general, Lozada of Colima—and wasn't he a terror? We made lots of money. General Lozada always had money with which to pay his soldiers, and I was a captain. I was an officer. When he fell short of money he would just gather in the haciendEros (ranchers) and he would say to them, 'Just so much money, I want it immediately. Send out and get it or tomorrow you die.' The money was always sure to come, and if it didn't, someone was surely shot in the morning, and then we would get our pay. As the next payday was approaching, the town merchants would be called upon. One time they 'kicked,' as the Americans say, and ten of the leading merchants were taken to the plaza and shot, and their stores sacked. And with this businesslike example, there was a very liberal contribution to the military fund by the tradespeople—those who had not already been shot. I was once sent with my company to a pueblo nearby, with orders to bring in so much money. I brought it, but before they would shell out I was compelled to execute two of the tradespeople of the town. I brought a priest to the plaza and threatened to have him shot, and didn't the rascal 'shell out? ' That's what the Americans call it here, Senor Espanol. They call it 'digging up' and 'shelling out.' I was lieutenant at the time but so well pleased was the general by my success that he at once promoted me to captain. Ah! A great man was General Lozada."

"I think," said the Spaniard, "I will buy the Simi ranch and perhaps El Rancho Tapo also, and I will show them in California how to manage an estate. How would you like to be my majordomo, Senor? I will pay a good salary. I want a man of your get-up, your caliber," and thus the conversation went on until it became time for Senor Muyoscuro to take his departure.

The horse was harnessed to the buggy, and the question was asked, "What amount will the reckoning be?"

"Why, not one cent, Senor, not one cent. I have been so greatly honored by your visit and your company that I would be glad to see you return. Everything pertaining to my ranch, myself included, is at your service henceforth. Come when you can, remain as long as you please. My house is your house, my land is your land. My horses and my mules and my burro are yours—except I no longer have horses, mules, burros, or cattle. That thief Leonis has them all. Ah! how I would liked to have had him down in Colima when I served under Lozada. Wouldn't I have made tamales of him! Well, I guess I will make tamales of him yet. The man has treated me scandalously."

By this time Muyoscuro had seated himself in his buggy, with lines and whip in hand.

"Senor," he said, "I would like to see you in Los Angeles. You could assist me very materially in the selection of a good ranch. As I tell you, I have plenty of money. Here, take this twenty dollars to pay your expenses to Los Angeles," at the same time passing a twenty-dollar gold piece.

"Here is my card, Senor," the Spaniard continued. "When you come to Los Angeles, call on me. I sympathise greatly with you at the way you have been treated by this bandit Leonis, and I will take care of you, Senor. I will help you get other horses and other stock. When can you call upon me in Los Angeles?"

"Whenever you say, Senor."

"Well then, suppose you come to town on Saturday. On Sunday, after mass, we will have a good talk. I always go to mass and I suppose you do, too. If you had really killed the priest down in Mexico that you talked about, I guess they would have excommunicated you, wouldn't they? So it must be that you didn't kill him—I am very glad of that. While sometimes priests deserve killing, in war times as well as others, it still is not very safe for one to kill a priest. So, adios, I will see you on Saturday." Senor Muyoscuro cracked his whip and headed eastward toward Los Angeles.

Leonis

23

The Cavern of the Dead—Discovery of its Treasures

T he old chief Odon was becoming sick and sore. He had been confined to his house—a well-furnished, plastered and whitewashed cottage that had been built for him by Leonis as an expression of his love and gratitude. Miguel had come to love Odon as though the old Indian were his father.

One morning Odon appeared in the warmth of the genial sunshine, looking cheerful and sprightly. "My good friend and patron," he said to Miguel, "come, seat yourself here with me on this well-worn granite stone. Many a time have I rested on this stone. And if you will look at it, patron, you will see that it is worn down into a groove—two grooves. This has been used for many, many years. Indians call it the trysting place. When we numbered our people by the thousands, there was never a morning or an evening that we did not see lovers seated upon this stone. When a young man and a maiden were observed seated here, it was indicative that they intended to marry. Sometimes the old Indians would come here with their wives in the cool of the evenings, to talk over their matters and tell stories of olden times. Many is the time I sat here with my wife when she was a maiden. Alas! Don Miguel, how I miss her. I have often thought how many long, long years this stone has been used as a trysting place. "Tradition has it," the old Indian continued, "the great spirit put this stone here, and that it has magic powers. It is said that if one is about to undertake an enterprise, he should come here to ponder over it—and if his mind runs smoothly it is an omen of success. But if anything irritates him while he is seated here or he is rudely interrupted by the arrival of an unwelcome person, it is ominous of evil and he should defer his undertaking until a more propitious time. But what I wish to talk with you about is this: I want you to accompany me to the Cavern of the Dead. I feel that my days are numbered, patron. My blood does not circulate as before, my joints have become stiff, and my limbs are always cold. I want to visit the cavern in your company, and I desire that we go today, for perhaps tomorrow I will be unable to do so. When we arrive there, patron, I will tell you the reason why I have urged you to accompany me. Will you do it?"

"Certainly, Odon. I will be ready within an hour. Get yourself ready. It is a beautiful day and we will go."

An hour later, the great Pyrenean giant and the relic of a ancient race were wending their way through the sinuosities of the mountain crags and passes. As before, they found their way through the interior of the cavern until they arrived among the tombs of the dead from centuries past.

They sat down, and Leonis produced a canteen full of wine, some cheese, onions, cold boiled eggs and bread, and the two partook of the noon-day luncheon. Odon then rose to his feet and wound his way among the numerous tombs, until he came to one in particular.

"My father told me," Odon said, "as he had been told by his father and those who preceded him, that this tomb was left without a tenant because it was constructed to receive the last chief of our race. That is, the last one who had a claim on the chieftanship, and my father said to me, 'You are the last in the line—here you are to be interred.'"

Leonis was about to test the solidity of the massive granite lid, which fitted so precisely on the raised sarcophagus, when Odon restrained him.

"Not yet, patron," he said. "Perhaps tomorrow or the next day, but not now. I know that with your great strength you can remove it, but

I do not want to view the interior of this tomb. I want to exact a promise from you that, when my spirit shall have departed this old tenement, you will bring my body here, remove this slab, and place me in the tomb of my fathers. It is the tomb my most remote ancestors intended for me, for alas! I am the last of my race."

Leonis was much affected by the gravity of the occasion, the grandeur of the surroundings, and the solemn tones in which Odon spoke. For some time, he could make no response. Then, recovering himself, he took the sad old Indian in his arms and embraced him as though he were a child—promising that, of course, Odon's request would be religiously complied with.

The shadows of the afternoon had fallen on the eastern slope of the mountain when the two made their descent back to the Escorpion ranch house. A good supper awaited them, after which Odon, greatly fatigued and unable to walk, was carried by Leonis and laid upon his bed. After the usual parting salutations of adios and buenos noches, Leonis returned to his own house to sleep.

The next morning he thought to call on the old Indian again, and found him dead. A problem presented itself—how could Leonis take the body to the cavern without the knowledge of the rest of the household? The mystery of the cave was Odon's secret, not theirs. Now the old Indian was dead, and Miguel felt he had no right to make known the wonders that he had revealed to him. To remove the body in daytime seemed out of the question, to remove it at night was more impossible still, since Miguel knew that in the darkness he would not be able to find his way to the cave entrance.

Locking Odon's door as he left the house, Miguel put the key in his pocket and went to his breakfast. While pondering over the situation, he suggested a picnic—a visit to the village of Rogerio at the Cienega of San Fernando. He ordered his men to hitch up the teams and informed his household that they would travel in wagons, while he rode on horseback.

"We must leave early," he told them.

It was understood that Odon would not be strong enough to go, so nothing was said about him. It took three wagons to carry the household. Leonis mounted his horse and rode alongside. After they were well on their way, he told them he had forgotten something at the ranch, that they should go ahead and wait for him at the Cienega.

Hurrying back to the ranch, he went to Odon's room and wrapped him in a clean winding sheet and blankets. He carried the body under one arm, and with the other he brought his refreshments, a large ball of strong twine, matches, candles, and a lantern. Soon he started rapidly up the mountainside toward the entrance of the cavern.

Slowly and with much difficulty, Leonis made his way with his great burden until he reached the interior of the cave. From there it was easy progress to the tombs and the particular one he sought. He laid Odon's body down carefully and rested. As he sat on a sarcophagus, he refreshed himself from his canteen and thought about the solemnity, grandeur and peculiarity of the situation.

As he recovered from his revery, he straightened up and tried to remove the stone covering of the tomb. To his surprise, he found he could not move it. It seemed to be cemented in place. There was but one thing to do. He returned hurriedly to the entrance to the cave and headed back to the ranch house for a chisel, hammer and crowbar. It was now well on toward noon.

Miguel ran rapidly, leaping from rock to rock, across chasms and ravines as nimbly and sure-footed as a mountain goat. Arriving at the ranch house, he found that he had made the distance in less than a half hour. He hastily secured the implements and returned to the cave, having made the entire trip in a little more than an hour and a half. His watch indicated the hour was one o'clock p.m.

Once back inside the Cavern of the Dead, Miguel used his steel-pointed crowbar as he sought to remove the lid of the sarcophagus. So neatly was it fitted, however, that he could not insert even the point. He therefore took his chisel and hammer and cut into the seam where the lid fitted to the body of the structure. Having improvised a fulcrum, he again tried his crowbar—but still the lid would not lift. Miguel made another cut, and another and another and still another, trying each one separately for he did not wish to break the stone slab in the process of removing it. Finally he felt the lid give way very slightly, and he tried the next opening he had made, and then another, and by the time he got around the lid it was loosened. Much as he tried to pry it aside, he found it would not move sideways. He finally raised it sufficiently to insert his chisel and then his hammer—only then did he ascertain that the lid had stone dowels two or three inches long, on the inside, which fit neatly into holes.

Miguel succeeded in raising the lid high enough to move it to one side, when he was almost suffocated by the effluvia that escaped from the interior of the tomb. So strong was the odor that he was compelled to stop and rest for a time, until the air dissipated. He then removed the lid, sliding it over until very nearly half of the opening was uncovered. He took his lantern and looked in. The bottom of the tomb was covered with white dust or ashes. Although there was no sign to indicate that a human body had been interred there—other than the dust of the ashes—he was convinced there had once been a body confined in the airtight tomb.

Lighting some tallow candles, Miguel set them inside. Then, with the chisel, he began to stir the ashes, when lo! he struck something metallic. Reaching in, he took up a mass of heavy metal, weighing perhaps a pound, and brushed the dust from it. He took it to the edge of the underground lake, where he washed the object clean and rubbed it dry on his sleeve. In the lantern's light, the sight of the gleaming molded image took his breath away—it was a golden grizzly. Returning to the tomb, Miguel stirred among the ashes again until he found another image, that of a buffalo. Next he found a mountain lion, a cougar, a civet, reptiles of various sorts, several birds—including a ground owl—and, the last and smallest, an exact replica of a horned toad. When he had collected all these things from the bottom of the tomb, he estimated their total weight to be fifty pounds, and his astonishment knew no limit.

"If the contents of this tomb is average for all the ones in the cavern, and these images truly are made of pure gold, then I have wealth enough here to ransom all of my country without bloodshed. I can buy the Basque people's independence from France and Spain!"

Suddenly remembering his mission, Miguel lifted the body of Odon, carefully set it inside the ancient tomb and fitted down the lid. He then stopped long enough to smoke a cigar, and filled the sleeves of his shirt to carry his treasures. Hastily retracing his steps to the mouth of the cavern, he returned to the ranch.✌

24

The Corral Del Los Burros—Miguel Hides the Gold

Upon his arrival at the Escorpion, Miguel hid the golden images and then stopped to rest and refresh himself. Harnessing a horse, he hitched it to a buggy and drove swiftly to the Cienega of San Fernando, village of the old chief Rogerio, where the fiesta was being held. The drive was fifteen miles but, having a good horse and being very excited and elated in spirit, Miguel covered the distance inside of two hours. He found his Escorpion people participating in the festivities of the occasion eating, drinking, listening to music, dancing and playing games—especially monte, the Mexican banking game, which they played for money. It was, in fact, as much the national game of Mexico as poker is for the Americans.

Excusing himself for his delay in coming, Leonis announced that he must leave again because he had to go to Los Angeles the next morning on important business. Taking Jule Drieux with him, he returned to the Escorpion, arriving soon after midnight.

After breakfast the next morning, when Drieux had gone out to inspect the herds, Leonis took a bucket of cement, a trowel, and an empty barley sack, and hurriedly made his way back to the cavern. Upon reaching the tomb in which he had placed the body of Odon, he mixed his cement and sealed the lid shut. Then, satisfied that he had down his work well, he rested, drank from his canteen, and smoked a cigar. Miguel then opened another tomb, which like the first contained golden images, and from it he extracted about twenty-five pounds in weight. Having satisfied himself that all the tombs contained more or less the same number of golden images—and that their removal was only a question of labor and was his for the taking,[1] Miguel returned to the ranch.

Drieux was preparing the noon-day meal, and Leonis took pains to explain to him how he had been exploring the surroundings of a site called the "corral de los burros," with a view to establishing a camp at the place. The corral was a crater-shaped valley some knew as "Sal si Puedes" (get out if you can). In former times, the Indians had used this place to conceal their livestock, particularly their burros. These nimble, sure-footed little fellows would climb down the crags of the precipitous sides of the ancient crater, and then could get out again. For mules, the feat was possible but uncertain. You might get a horse down to the valley-like bottom but you couldn't get him out again, so this was a sure place to corral burros. At the bottom was an area of good grass and timber, covering as much as one or two hundred acres of good land, with water trickling from the mountain crags. It was a very nice place for the keeping of burros.

Leonis explained to Drieux that he planned to cut a road down the sides of the extinct crater to the bottom, and there he intended to establish a ranch. He would build a house, cultivate the ground, store up grass and hay, and use the place as a refuge in times of short pasturage. This, he told Drieux, had been his occupation all that day, for he intended to go to Los Angeles to bring back a force of laborers with blasting powder and materials—in order to start work at once on the enterprise.

"Have you ever been down inside the corral de los burros?" Leonis asked Drieux. "No? Well, it is the most remarkable place I have ever seen in my life. The bottom is almost level—with plenty of water all around the rim of the basin—and the land is of a most fertile character. Today the grass stood two feet high. Were it raked and baled into hay, it would produce three tons to the acre. Just think of it! And the lone oaks that dot the surface are so beautiful, the place is a paradise—cool in summer and warm in winter.

"You would think," continued Leonis, "that in the heat of summer a basin of this sort would grow intensely hot, but there is a circulation of cool air coming from openings in the rocky sides of the rim. It feels as though there were a thousand fans stirring the air. And it is not a wind that blows in any particular direction or a draft of air. This is a constant circulation of pure, cool air, as though from thousands of fans all operating at once. If I were to pass the rest of my life in this beautiful country—and I wish it could be so, but destiny has ordained otherwise—I would build me a palace in this fantastic spot, and I would be like one of the kings we read about in ancient fables. After dinner, Drieux, I will go to Los Angeles for the preparations for road making. We must make the corral de los burros useful to us. It is more beautiful to behold when you climb down the rocky crags and obtain a sure footing at the bottom. Of course, although it is a good place for burros, the fact is that burros are not a commercial commodity. They are of little use except to Indians and miners, and they are not saleable except in small numbers, one and two at a time for ten or fifteen dollars each. But oh! what a place for the rearing of fine horses. Once we construct a good road, I intend to have it."

Loading his buggy with the sackful of golden images, Leonis drove to Los Angeles, and stopped at the Tendajon de la Campana to call on Mascarel. He was not home. "Mascarel left this morning for Santa Barbara," he was told. "He will be absent for a week."

It had been Miguel's intention to show Mascarel his treasures and ask for his help in devising a secret means of removing the numerous remaining images, which he conjectured were still in the cavern, concealed in the multitude of ancient tombs. He was greatly disappointed to learn of Mascarel's absence.

Continuing to his orchard house located on Aliso Street,[2] Miguel tied up his horse, removed his sack of treasures—along with other things he had in the buggy—and, while his house servants tended to his horse and prepared supper, he quietly inserted the treasure sack under the front

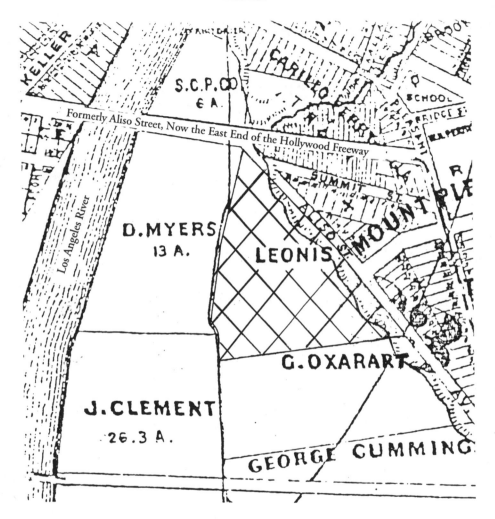

Leonis' 17¹/₂ acre "Orchard" in East Los Angeles. The house was at the north end, facing Summit Street "G. Oxarart" was also a French Basque.

steps of his house until he could see Mascarel. He was well aware that it would require the wisdom, sagacity and business efficiency of Mascarel to manage the massive proportions of the great enterprise that recovering the golden images presented. He estimated there might be tons of solid gold in the cavern, which had to be converted into coin of equivalent value. Perhaps Mascarel might dispose of the treasure at the United States mint in exchange for goverment certificates for the dollar value—without making known the discovery or being detected. If the story were ever to be found out, certainly it would cause a revolution. American adventurers, gold seekers, and all manner of the restless class would tear the mountain asunder in order to participate in the removal of this wonderful wealth.☙

Endnotes

1. This story has the flavor of an ancient Mexican legend. Horace Bell spent some time in Mexico—he joined the army of Benito Juarez in 1859, to fight against the reactionary president Miguel Miramon for Mexico's freedom.

2. Miguel Leonis owned 17 ½ acres of orchard property in the east Los Angeles suburb known as Boyle Heights. His house was located on Summit Avenue, a street described in *Fortune Favors The Brave* as the "right-hand termination of old Aliso street (that) came down a hill from the east suburbs." (p.213) The earliest city directory listing of this house appears in 1888, "Miguel Leonis, orchardist, res(idence) S(outh) s(ide) Summit Ave. nr. Anderson, Boyle Heights."

   A Sanborn Fire Insurance map of the area, dated 1894, indicates the structure was a single-story, wood-frame residence with a brick basement and a wood shingle roof. The house had a bridge of sorts, which connected like a T to the middle of the two-story front porch. This porch had steps leading from its east end to a still-opened side street—an indication the structure was not on level ground.

   Most of Summit Avenue no longer exists, having been removed years ago for the construction of the freeway. The site of Miguel's house is probably covered by the housing project presently known as Aliso Village.

Leonis

25

An Assassin's Perfect Weapon—Six Mile House
Miguel's Words Overheard

n the day Leonis arrived in Los Angeles with his sack of golden images, Saldanyoseguro also had gone to the city—where he immediately presented himself at the Spanish secret agent's apartments in the Pico House.[1]

"I am very glad to see you, Senor," said Muyoscuro. "What news do you bring of the bandit Leonis? Is he still as bad as ever? As domineering to poor people of your class? Or has someone settled his hash, as should have been done in Pyrenean Spain years ago?"

"He came to town this morning—passed me on the way, at the Six Mile House. He stopped there and watered his horses. I watched him while he drank his wine and gossiped with Etchepare and Labaig without so much as asking me to take a drink of beer. May lightning strike him! After having stolen all of my horses, cattle and burros!"

"We will keep a watch on him," said the Spaniard, "and, when he returns to the Escorpion, you must ride out with him."

"I, ride with him! Why he would not carry me ten yards of my way were my legs cut off above the knees!"

"Oh, yes, he will—and it may well be his last trip anywhere. Certainly, if I were you and should have such an opportunity, I would see that he never reached the end of his journey."

"I would like to see to that," said Saldanyoseguro, "if only he would take me—and if I had a means to put an end to that scoundrel."

Bruce Torrence Historical Collection.

The "Six Mile House," so called because it was six miles from Los Angeles, in those days, stood at the northeast corner of Sunset and Gower, in what is now downtown Hollywood. It was operated by two French Basques, Etchepare and Labaig.

"We can fix that. Get yourself ready, and when he leaves the city you must await him in the Cahuenga Pass. I have some clothes for you to disguise yourself—here is the garb of a Franciscan friar. All you must do is pretend to be fatigued and languish by the roadside. When Leonis passes along in his wagon, you beg him to carry you part of your way. Say that you are a friar going to the monastery at Santa Barbara. Of course, he will be polite to a friar and invite you to take a seat beside him. Observe, Senor, here is a very small pistol, which carries a little conical bullet half the size of a pea. The gun is smokeless and noiseless when fired—a little instrument that has taken the place of the dagger in Spain—but you have to know how to use it. I will teach you. Take hold of it, Senor. Now, pull the trigger—but don't point it at me—and let the bullet lodge in the wall. When you pull the trigger, without any noise or smoke, the delicate projectile will become imbedded in the hard plaster of this brick wall."

"You will see," instructed the Spaniard, "that to make sure work and avoid any possibility of detection, you must place the muzzle of this little pistol in the very hollow of a man's ear. It will not only kill him almost instantly, but has the advantage of leaving not the least sign for a coroner to act upon. There will be no blood, no outer wound—and the coroner's verdict will be that the man died of apoplexy or heart failure."

Muyoscuro smiled and continued, "Do you think you can manage this little fellow, Senor? If you should fail, you know what will come of it. If you should succeed—do you see this box?" pointing to a box on the table, "There is one thousand dollars in there, in gold coin. If you should succeed, come here directly and this box shall be yours. Now then, I will give you a hundred extra dollars to start upon, and when I buy the Simi ranch, I will make you majordomo-in-chief. I intend to buy the Virgines, too, and also the Escorpion. Here is another twenty dollars, for spending money. Keep an eye on Leonis and find out when he will depart the city."

Three days later, Saldanyoseguro went to the Spaniard's apartments to report that Leonis was leaving for the Escorpion that same day, in the cool of the evening. He had heard that Leonis was taking ranch supplies and would go alone, driving his own two-horse wagon.

At the time appointed for Leonis' departure, the Spaniard drove around town in a buggy—the mock friar seated beside him—and passed the stable where Miguel awaited the harnessing of his horses. The two drove around for some time, keeping an eye on Leonis until he started, and then they rattled out of town on a different road to the Cahuenga Pass. Dropping off the friar at the pass, Muyoscuro returned to the Six Mile House, where he had his team stabled for a rest and seated himself to a glass of wine and a fragrant Havana.

Inside of half an hour Leonis drove up to the station, had his horses watered, refreshed himself and stood a few minutes. Then he drove leisurely toward the pass.

The Spaniard decided to eat his supper at the Six Mile House. Madam Labaig had promised him some young pigeons, and he rather liked observing the company that came and went—this being a favorite resort for afternoon drives from Los Angeles. While the Spaniard sipped his wine and smoked, two men drove up in a buggy. As they alighted, one of them remarked to the other as they approached the cantina.

"Bisc, have you a spare dollar?"

"Oh! go to the devil, Dick. Come in and fill yourself with wine and I will pay for it, but stop that dollar business! I am sick and tired of it."

As soon as the two entered, Mulligan hung himself on the counter, all but suspended from it by virtue of his projecting chin. It was close to sundown. Soon others arrived, and there was quite an assembly in the tap room and in the cattle sheds surrounding the house. As it became dark and the lamps were lighted, a man suddenly ran in. He was greatly excited—breathless and speechless—and though he tried to communicate, he could not articulate the words.

Labaig gave him a glass of brandy, to settle him down so he could tell what he had to say. Finally, he got it out, "Don Miguel Leonis is lying dead on the road near the summit of the pass! His horses and wagon are standing near by."

There was great excitement at the cantina. Labaig and Etchepare hurried to hitch the horses to their vehicle and then sprang into it, with others following as they rushed to the place where the body was reported to be lying. There they found Miguel weltering in his blood—for the wagon wheels had passed over his face. The horses stood still close by. Hastily lifting the bleeding victim into the wagon—Etchepare holding his head and Labaig driving—they returned to the cantina. Others took charge of Leonis' team and led the horses back at a more leisurely pace.[2]

Despite his injuries, Miguel Leonis did not die immediately. Breathing heavily, he tried to speak. He was carried in, laid upon a bed, and some brandy forced down his throat. Wet towels were applied to his head, and the blood and dirt sponged from his face. The room was cleared of the crowd that had surrounded him, but Biscailuz remained. After a time, and with great effort, Leonis spoke.

Cahuenga Pass, from the top looking South towards Hollywood,
1899.

"Mascarel," he said.

"Mascarel is in Santa Barbara," Madam Labaig told him.

Miguel indicated that he knew that.

"Have you a message for Mascarel?"

Miguel nodded.

"What shall I tell Mascarel?"

"Search under stairway front orchard house. Great value." Miguel spoke in the Basque language so that only the Labaigs and Etchepare could understand him. But, standing at the far end of the room, Biscailuz also understood.

At once Biscailuz returned to the tap room to look for Mulligan.

"Come, Dick, let's go," he told him. "Not a word. I will explain once we are on the road." And the two leading Los Angeles lawyers jumped into their buggy. Biscailuz cracked the whip, and away they sped for the six miles it took to reach Los Angeles. As soon as they had got well under way, Biscailuz explained what he had heard to Mulligan.

"We must go to the orchard house and search under the stairway. We may find something, Dick!"

In order to reach the orchard house of Leonis, they had to cross the river.[3] Tying up their horses, the two men crossed the riverbed on foot. It happened, however, that at about the time they tied up their horses, they were observed by El Diablo—Manuel Dominguez. Dominguez had just settled in for the night at Leonis' house, where he had been left in charge until Leonis' next visit from the Escorpion.

When the two lawyers arrived and walked to the front of the house, Manuel took position to see who they were and what they were up to. Although it was dark, he immediately recognized Biscailuz and soon after recognized the distinctive head of Richard Mulligan.

"This way," said Bisc furtively. "I know the house as well as I do my own. Ah! many is the cup of wine I have enjoyed here. Leonis kept good wine, I tell you, and good brandy as well. But here we are at the stairway. The stairs go up on the outside, you know. Now, I will just lay down and reach under this step and yes! I have got it, Dick! And I think I know what it is! This is heavy!" He spoke in low tones as he slowly dragged something from under the stairway.

Mulligan went to pick it up. "Bisc, I can't lift it!" he whispered. "It's done up in cords and gunny sacks. Here, you take one end and I will take the other. When we get away from the house, we will see what it is."

From his position around the corner of the house, only a few feet away, Manuel Dominguez watched the two worthies make their way to the road and start toward their buggy.

"It is gold, I am sure it is gold!" Mulligan said. "I'll bet it is twenty dollar gold pieces. And from the heft of it, there must be twenty thousand dollars in here. Great grizzly, Bisc! What a find we have. Come on, let's go.!"

"Go where?" asked Bisc.

"To the buggy and then we can go over to my house."

"What! To your house! Away over in Poverty Flat—or Hobo Hollow, or wherever it is you live!? Well, I am not going there. Let's take it up to my house. My house is less than a quarter of a mile, your Hobo Roll is three miles from here. A great place for a lawyer to live, Dick! Come on, let's go. We will take the treasure to my house, and open it up and see what it is."

"No," said Mulligan. "I am going to take it to my house if it takes all night."

"Well, I am going to take it to my house," and Biscailuz heaved up the weighty sack and placed upon his shoulder. Whereupon Mulligan grabbed hold of it, and the two fell to the ground with the sack between them. A great fighting and pulling and hauling and pounding ensued. Mulligan grabbed Biscailuz by the throat, while Biscailuz had Mulligan by the hair, drew him down and commenced beating him on the face. The two were howling—absolutely mad with rage. After several minutes, having exhausted their strength, their resolve, and their anger, they mutually declared a truce and straightened themselves for a parley. Mulligan was the first to speak.

"Very well, Bisc, I will give in to you, for once in my life. We will take our find to your house and see what it is," and he turned to pick up the sack. "Why, Bisc, where is it?"

Bisc felt around with his foot. "Why, I don't know." he said. "It ought to be right here. Right here's where we had the fight and right here we let it fall."

He struck a match and searched the ground. He struck another match and searched the ground. Striking a third match, he searched the ground in a greater circle. Mulligan tried to strike a match, but his nerves were so unsettled he could not do it. The treasure was gone.

While the two leading lawyers had been fighting over the heavy sack, Manuel had picked it up, thrown it over his muscular shoulder, and stepped out of the way—without the two worthies noticing his presence.

Very soon, Manuel was trudging in the sands of the Los Angeles river, convinced in his mind that it was gold coin he was carrying and deliberating where to carry it to. He resolved to take it to the house of his mother, Dona Chica.

Dona Chica lived at the foot of the hill away out on Castellar Street, and to get there Manuel would have to make a wide circuit if he did not want to be seen going through town with such a burden upon his shoulder. He followed the riverbed until he passed the point where the Mission road crossed the river. Then, he skirted the northern end of Sonora Town until at last he arrived at the open space of ground fronting his mother's house; the house standing some distance back from the street.

It had been an excessively hot September day, and now the evening was sultry. After covering a distance of nearly three miles—most of it through the deep sand of the riverbed—Manuel was utterly fagged out. He stood in front of Dona Chica's house and had just laid down his burden, intending to draw some water from the well to refresh himself, when lo! he heard footsteps approach. Thinking he was pursued, he dropped the heavy sack into the well. Then he turned toward the direction of the footsteps and found himself confronted by a man—and they grappled with each other.

Now who was this man? From where did he come and how did it happen that he so inopportunely encountered Manuel in this place at this unreasonable hour? No houses were immediately near, and the few of them at that end of Sonora Town were scattered far apart.

Let us go back to the Cahuenga Pass—when Saldanyoseguro stopped the wagon and set the brake, a short distance from where Miguel Leonis lay, and plunged into the chaparral that covered the craggy mountainside. It was already dusk, and as he pushed through the thickest of the chaparral for some distance, he began to mutter to himself, "I guess

I did that as well as the most artistic assassin in Spain! Now it is over. The bandit is dead, and I will make my way to town. I will go to the Pico House and get my thousand dollars in gold—no one will be the wiser for it." Stopping to rest, he divested himself of the monk's robe, drew from the folds of his shirt a well-worn slouch hat, and started anew for the city.

When night fell, it became very hard traveling over the rough mountain crags and through the thorny chaparral. But after an hour's hard and persevering effort, he reached the smooth hills lying between the Cahuenga valley and Los Angeles, where travel was easy, and so he hurried on. He was famished for water. Remembering that there was a well at Dona Chica's house, he thought he would rest and refresh himself there. To his surprise, however, he was intercepted. A man lay in wait for the purpose of arresting him. In desperation, he seized his assailant and the two grappled on the ground. In their struggle for mastery, each man was as powerful as the other—until Saldanyoseguro's hand came in contact with a piece of wood. It was one of those oak pieces split up for stove wood, and, raising himself with all his strength, he gave his assailant a terrible blow on the head. It knocked the man senseless and left him prone upon the ground.

Saldanyoseguro made his way through the dark streets of Sonora Town and to the Pico House. Directly he went to the apartments of Senor Muyoscuro and knocked at the door, but it elicited no response. It was now quite late. He walked up and down the hall and repeated his knocks at two or three intervals—but with the same result. Finally, he came out to the sidewalk, where he took a seat near the hotel entrance to anxiously await the arrival of his patron. But the Spaniard did not come. It was now nine o'clock at night, and so he went to the hotel proprietor's office to inquire as to his patron's whereabouts.

"When will El Senor Muyoscuro be in?"

"He has left the house," the hotel clerk responded.

"Has left the house? When?"

"Just a little while ago."

"When will he be back?"

"I don't think he will come back at all. He took all his baggage and was driven down to the train—the train to San Francisco, I think. Let me check yes, he is gone. He paid his bill. An odd character this fellow was. I can't imagine what kind of business he had here, but he stayed about the hotel for a month or two. And he had plenty of money. What do you know about him?"

"He is a rich Spaniard, who came here for the purpose of buying a large ranch. He had plenty of money, and I was supposed to make inquiries for him. He was about to buy the Simi ranch. I imagine he will come back soon."

The crestfallen Mexican slowly walked into the bar and bought himself a drink—laying down a twenty-dollar gold piece to be changed.

"Why, my good fellow," said the barkeeper, "have you been drawing on the United States mint?"

"Oh! explained Saldanyoseguro, "the rich Spaniard gave me twenty dollars to pay my expenses while I ran errands for him. He was very good to me. I am sorry he has gone. I hope he will be back."

The next morning Manuel Dominguez was found wandering in a demented condition through the streets of Sonora Town—his head very bloody and swollen. The policeman who found him recognized who he was and took him to his mother's house, where his wound was cared for and he was put to bed. He could not tell anyone what had hurt him. All he could say was "mucho dinero" (a lot of money), and then he would ask "Where is my money—the great bag of gold that I carried?"

Manuel would then go off into a stupor and, when he came to, he would repeat the same words. His mind wandered, and all he would talk about was gold and money and ask what had become of his. When questioned as to what money he had lost, he would say there were wagonloads of it. A doctor was called in, who pronounced him as suffering from a concussion of the brain. For weeks Manuel lay in bed with a high fever, his mind befogged, all the time struggling to explain something about his gold. But Dominguez was a strong fellow. As the weeks and months passed, he gradually recovered. His appetite improved and his physical strength returned. He could remember that he had had a big bag of gold—but where he got it and what he had done with it, he could not recall. And he had no recollection of the fight or the blow he received on his head. Manuel went on to live for years, and his mind did not improve a particle on the subject.

When the dying Leonis had been brought to Labaig's Six Mile House, Muyoscuro got in his buggy and left for Los Angeles, satisfied that the work he had been sent from Spain to accomplish had been done well. He had long since discarded the ex-friar Jean Pierre and rather rejoiced when Goytino was locked up in the county jail of Los Angeles— he was glad to be rid of him. Once back in Los Angeles, the Spaniard settled his bill at the Pico House, called a hack and had his trunk removed. Then he left quickly for the railroad station, where he arrived just in time to take the train to San Francisco. He was hurrying back to Spain to report his progress to the Minister of Justice. He did not leave a thousand-dollars in a box for Saldanyoseguro. ✕

Endnotes

1. The Pico House was a sumptuous hotel constructed by Pio Pico in 1869. For the decade that followed, it was considered the finest hotel south of San Francisco. Located on the corner of Main and Plaza streets, on the former site of the old Carillo adobe, this three-storied structure had deep-set arched windows and doors, and walls of stuccoed brick painted to resemble pale blue granite.

   The exterior was restored some 15 or 20 years ago, but controversy has kept the interior unrestored and the building unoccupied to this day (1991).

2. In city newspaper accounts, the incident leading to Leonis' death was reported as an accident. Horace Bell refused to accept this, and for years he maintained his personal belief that Leonis had been murdered by one of his numerous enemies.

On September 23, 1889, the *Los Angeles Daily Herald* published the inquest testimony of Juan Jose Melendez [a misspelling of Menendez—this was Espiritu's son by Jose Antonio Menendez]. Menendez testified that on September 17 he and four others had accompanied Leonis on the journey from Los Angeles to Calabasas, and that the party had been in good spirits—singing and joking to relieve the tedium of the long trip. At about 6:00 p.m. they had reached the point in the Cahuenga where the dummy railroad track crossed the road—several miles outside of Los Angeles [not the Cahuenga Pass]—when the wagon in which Leonis was riding was jerked by the jolting of the wheels. Leonis fell from the front seat over the side of the wagon and between the wheels. Before they could stop the wagon, one of the rear wheels rolled over his abdomen, chest and face. He was picked up, bleeding profusely and evidently in great agony. They laid him upon blankets on the wagon and, at his request, he was taken to the house of Martin Etchepare. (The 6 Mile House; Ed.)

Menendez' testimony continued that Dr. Nadeau was sent for, and the doctor concluded that Leonis had suffered four broken ribs and several internal injuries from which there was no hope of recovery. Traumatic peritonitis set in, and Leonis died on September 20, 1889. He was buried in the old cemetery at the north end of what was then Eternity Street (now Grand Avenue) just north of downtown Los Angeles. When this cemetery was abandoned, and the bodies removed, Leonis' body and that of his daughter, Marcelina, were moved to a family plot in Calvary Cemetery in East Los Angeles.

3. The Los Angeles river separates Los Angeles from its east suburb of Boyle Heights. Subject to flash floods in the winter, it dried up com-

pletely in the summer—other than for occasional water holes in the riverbed.

26

Biscailuz and Mulligan Find the Sack
Dominguez Meets Saldanyoseguro

n the day following the tragic event at the Cahuenga Pass, and their failure to keep possession of the treasure found under the front steps of Leonis' house, Richard Mulligan called on his friend Biscailuz and they communed.

"Do you have a spare dollar, Bisc? I am just dying for at least a half dozen drinks. My stomach is full of crawfish and my head is bursting and burning up. My throat is swollen and sore where you choked me, Bisc. I want a dollar. I want to go down to Jake Philippi's and fill up."

"You don't want to get drunk sooner than four o'clock, do you, Dick? You would scandalize the town if you fill up in the morning. Or is it possible for you to get full before four o'clock? I'll tell you what I'll do. We will go down to Jake's and I will set 'em up for two rounds—and then we will come back here and talk. I still don't understand what became of that bag of gold that we fought over. How could it disappear so mysteriously? But I won't give you a dollar, not until we get through with this business—or whatever other business may come before the Court."

"What do you mean by 'come before the Court?'"

"Only that I am the Court and I want you to bring some business before it. We need clients, Dick. Come on, let's go and get our drinks. I am a little thirsty myself."

"Whiskey straight," ordered Mulligan.

S. F. B. M.

Vous êtes prié d'assister aux funérailles de

MIGUEL LEONIS,

Né à Cambo, Basses-Pyrénées (France) en 1824, décédé à Los Angeles le 20 Septembre 1889, à 6 heures du matin, à l'âge de 65 ans.

Le convoi funèbre partira de l'établissement Garret & Samson, rue North Main No. 234, lundi 23 Septembre, à 9 heures et demie du matin.

Service à la Cathédrale à 10 heures du matin.

De la part de:

Mme Espiritu Léonis, son épouse.
Jean Léonis, son neveu.

Jose Mascarel
John Roberts
George Lemesnager
Pierre Darancette
Célestin Save
A. Raynal
Léon Escallier
J. Daurias
J. B. Cohn
Mlle Marie Gassagne
N. Tellier
Jean Dubart

} Ses amis.

Los Angeles, 21 Septembre 1889.

Leonis Adobe Archives.

Miguel Leonis died on September 20, 1889. This is an invitation to his funeral, which was supposed to have been held at the Catholic Cathedral, which still stands on Main Street, Los Angeles. However, according to contemporary newspaper accounts the body was taken directly from the mortuary to the cemetery, and no mass was held.

"Pure absinthe," said Biscailuz—and the two worthies gazed at the ceiling.

About that time Haley came in, "Good morning, Mr. Mulligan. Good morning, Mr. Biscailuz. What will you have, gentlemen?"

"Whiskey. Straight."

"Pure absinthe."

For himself, Haley ordered a beer. "Have you heard the news?" he inquired.

"What news?"

"Don Miguel Leonis was killed out at Cahuenga Pass yesterday afternoon, and his body has just been brought to the morgue."

Stephen M. White, Attorney, later he, with Horace Bell, won Espiritu Leonis a widow's share of Miguel Leonis' estate.

"Yes, we heard about it. We saw him when he was brought in at Etchepare and Labaig's Six Mile House. The doctors were disputing over him when we left. We did not stay—we could do no good and we were very much horrified at the happening. We didn't even find out how it occurred, except they said it appeared that he had fallen off the wagon and a wheel had passed over his face."

"Well, well, well," said Haley, "there are going to be some fat pickings for lawyers. Leonis' estate is worth nearly a million dollars. I wonder if he left a will. I think he did—I seem to remember that John Robarts wrote his will some years ago. I think John is one of the executors, some Frenchman is the other, and Hellman."

"I wonder what he left Espiritu," all three said in an undertone.

"I think she ought to claim as the widow of Leonis. Honestly, I believe she could maintain her claim to wifehood, if it was fairly presented."

237

"Let's have another drink," said Mulligan, and Haley again set them up.

The trio separated, and Biscailuz and Mulligan returned to Biscailuz' office in Temple Block.

"Bisc, right there is the best money-making scheme that has presented itself yet! Let's take up Espiritu and have her file a claim as Leonis' wife. I understand he has brothers in France who will come in for half of the estate. Espiritu could claim the other half. Who will approach her about this? You and me?"

"Neither of us," said Biscailuz. "I have a better idea. I know a couple of half-breed Indians—the wife of a Frenchman and her brother. They have great influence with Espiritu. Whenever she comes to town, she always visits their house. Let's go and see them," and away they went.

As they walked, Mulligan remarked that "grass must not be permitted to grow under our feet. This is too big a thing to allow for delay or fooling."

Soon they arrived at the residence of Monsieur Pelitier, whose wife was a half-breed Indian—and it happened that her brother was also present in the house.[1] The two lawyers were informed that Espiritu was expected to arrive in the evening and that she would pass the night at the Pelitier house. The two worthies unfolded their plan, and everyone in the group thought there was something in it. Certainly it was worth at least a half million.

"Which lawyers should we take this to?" asked the two half-breed Indians.

A discussion ensued. Objections were made to the two lawyers present—both of whom disclaimed any real interest in representing Espiritu. Finally, it was decided that as soon as she came in—that night or immediately after Leonis' funeral—she should be brought to the office of Mr. Stephen M. White, a very prominent lawyer and a conscientious man, and he should be requested to present the housekeeper's claim.

"But where do we come in for our part of the spoil?" asked Biscailuz.

"That is exactly what I was thinking," said Mulligan.

Madam Pelitier's brother, who was a well-educated Indian, spoke up: "We will fix it this way. We will get as big a divvy with Mr. White as we can, and then we will divvy our share with you gentlemen. And we will all work together to get testimony, to prove Espiritu's wifehood."

The parties separated after having reached an understanding—and an agreement with Madam Pelitier and her brother Sylvanus that they would keep a strict surveillance of Espiritu. It was important that she not fall into the hands of designing persons, especially those of the legal fraternity. She was to be taken to Mr. White's office as soon as possible, where they would get the best contract out of him they could.

By then it was well on toward afternoon. "Now Bisc," said Mulligan, "I want that spare dollar. I promise you not to disgrace myself by getting drunk earlier than four o'clock. The fact is, there is not whiskey enough in town, if I drank it all, to make me drunk inside of two hours, and after four o'clock I have full license. No one expects to see me sober after four o'clock. The dollar, Bisc?"

"All right, Dick, here's the dollar. As we go along, let's stop at the Hotel Pyrenees and take a drink. We may get some news there."

When they had wetted up at the Hotel Pyrenees, the two worthies continued on their way to Jake Philippi's. There they met Robarts.

"Yes, I have Leonis' will," Robarts admitted. "I will deposit it with the Clerk of the Court tomorrow, and you can all see for yourselves. But I can tell you one thing, for it never has been a secret. At Hellman's Bank is twenty thousand dollars willed to Espiritu for being his 'faithful housekeeper.' As soon as the will is admitted to probate, the executors, of which I am one, are ordered to pay that over, not to Espiritu herself, but to deposit it, with the interest to be paid to her."

"Why doesn't she set up a claim to wifehood?" asked Mulligan.

"Some lawyer should take that up," answered Robarts. "I can give them lots of information—I can point out many witnesses who will support her claim. But still, having been named as an executor of the will, I can have no suggestions to make."

"I will take whiskey straight," said Mulligan.

"Pure absinthe," said Biscailuz.

"And I will have some of your best California port," said Robarts, and each man wetted his respective whistle.

They were about to retire when the barkeeper said, "Who pays for this round?"

"Why, Robarts, of course," answered Mulligan.

"Oh, get out!" said Robarts.cʌ

Endnotes

1. The two half Indians in this story may have been Constance Mascarel Tellier and her brother Sylvester Mascarel—named in Jose Mascarel's will as two of his three children still living as of the date of the will, September 16, 1899. These offspring were presumably by Cerilda, described in *Land of the West Valley* as a good friend of Espiritu. (p.)

Mascarel had at least six children, the four named in the will—Sylvester, Constance, Hortense and Maria Concepcion—and two whose names appear in city birth records, Petronila (born 1854) and Adolfo (born 1860). One of Mascarel's daughters eventually married Jean Pierre Goytino.

27

Espiritu Claims on the Estate

In his private office, the eminent lawyer Stephen M. White[1] was engaged in consultation with Mulligan, Biscailuz, Pelitier and his half-Indian wife, the wife's brother Sylvanus Mascarbo,[2] and Espiritu.

With the help of Sylvanus as interpreter, White addressed himself directly to the would-be widow of Miguel Leonis, "So, you wish to set up a claim that you are the wife of Miguel Leonis. Is that it?"

"Si, Senor," said Espiritu.

"What proof have you to sustain such a claim?"

"The whole world, sir. Everybody knows that Don Miguel Leonis said I was his wife. He put it in writing, and we can bring two hundred witnesses here to prove by his own statement that he always regarded me as his wife and said that I was his wife."

Mulligan chipped in, "I myself know more than twenty witnesses who will swear that Leonis always said that he was married to her."

"And I can bring twenty more," said Biscailuz.

"And I can bring two hundred additional witnesses, if necessary," said Pelitier, who was seconded in his assertion by his wife and by Sylvanus Mascarbo.

"If you will bring to my office ten, fifteen or twenty of your best and most reputable witnesses, I will examine them, take down their statements in writing, and then give you an answer as to whether or not I will take your case," he said to Espiritu.

241

"There is one thing that puzzles me," White remarked to Biscailuz and Mulligan. "In going through the files in the courthouse some time ago, I found a declaration in writing made by Espiritu—in which she denied all claims to wifehood in regard to Leonis, saying she always had been and still remained his housekeeper and nothing more. How are we to get over that?"

"We will see about that," said Mulligan. "We will produce the statement and show it to her, and we'll see what she has to say about it."

With Sylvanus Mascarbo acting as interpreter, crowds of witnesses were carefully examined by the lawyer White, and they were all judged as satisfactory—that their testimony would make out a good case. The question again came up about Espiritu's courtroom declaration, which had been filed during the suit between her father Odon and Leonis years before.

One day Mascarbo brought Espiritu to White's office and reported that when he, Mulligan and Biscailuz had shown the paper to her, after examining it, she had told them "it is wrong, it is a mistake." Espiritu was said to have informed them that what she had intended to tell the court—and actually did say—was that she was Leonis' wife and not his housekeeper, but that the man who wrote down her testimony got it wrong.

Mascarbo supported Espiritu's story, "The records show that I was the interpreter on that occasion, and I most solemnly declare that the document is wrong. It reversed that which she did say, and you can prove it by me if you wish."

When the will of Leonis had been probated, the twenty thousand dollars deposited at Hellman's bank was duly rendered to Espiritu for her acceptance—but she refused it, on the grounds that she was the widow of the deceased and therefore entitled to one half of the estate.

It must not be forgotten that Espiritu was the owner in her own right of the residence at Calabasas,[3] and that she had hundreds of head of horned cattle and horses of her own—so she was rich independently of what Leonis gave her or of what she might get out of his estate. With all of the legal formula made and provided by law, the lawyer Stephen M. White presented Espiritu's claim to the probate court.

The estate holdings were being assembled and appraised, and the records searched for titles and the like, when lo! the executors ran up against a legal Gibraltar. Leonis had died not owning one dollar's worth of property in California, real or personal! After he had drafted his will, Leonis conveyed all of his properties to Josef Mascarel. The stunning commotion this discovery caused was unprecedented. A million dollars' worth of property was escaping the clutches of all who grasped for it.

Miguel's brothers began arriving from the Pyrenees, the sisters, likewise, uncles, cousins and aunts came from Africa—all of them bent on possessing a part of the million. They wanted their shares, but no shares were to be had. Mascarel had purchased the whole of it and, when spoken to on the street about it, his only answer was, "Quien sabe?"

Eventually, the one-time mayor of Los Angeles,[4] by now the most ancient of the city fathers and the richest man in town, was brought into court to answer questions concerning his dealings with the deceased. The court wanted to know what consideration he had given for it—that is, how much money had he paid for this million dollars worth of property that now stood entirely in his name?

Without hesitation, the great Mascarel stated that he had not paid one dollar for it. He told the court that when the deed was made, Leonis contemplated a visit to the Pyrenees and thought it exceedingly doubtful that he would ever return. "The deed was made to me as a trust deed to hold the property for him," Mascarel explained. "I have it—not for my-self—but for his heirs. At the time Miguel Leonis died he did not owe me one dollar, and neither did I owe him."

This most astonishing confession, from a man whom some re-garded as an absolute grasping money-getter, was breathtaking news. It caused every one with knowledge of the affair to regard Jose Mascarel in the same way he regarded Isaiah Hellman—as absolutely honest and trustworthy.

The outcome of the whole affair was that, after thirty days' struggle in court and before a jury, a verdict was rendered, filed, entered and recorded, in which the court declared that Espiritu Chijulla had been married to Miguel Leonis, and that at the time of his death she was his wife and was now his widow. This made her the richest widow in Los Angeles county. After feeing the lawyers and others who had assisted her, Espiritu had at least three hundred thousand dollars interest in the estate of Miguel Leonis.[5]

"Good morning, Dick," said Biscailuz on the day after the trial, when Mulligan presented himself at his office. "How do you feel about the victory?"

"I feel glorious, Bisc. Have you a spare dollar? You know, I kept sober all of last week and the week before and the week before that—which is to say, I kept sober until after four o'clock and I was always bright and fresh when court opened in the morning. But now I want to have a good fill. Bisc, I want that dollar."

"I am thinking of something more serious, Mr. Mulligan," said Biscailuz. "I want to know where and how we are going to come in for our share of Espiritu's recovery. Mr. White is to get half of it and that will only leave her about three hundred thousand dollars. What will White give us? Sylvanus Mascarbo says that White is to divide even with him, yet we have no claim on either him or his sister."

"I will tell you what to do, Bisc. You should see some of those Leonis brothers and sisters and such like kinsfolk, who now infest our street corners, and get contracts from them. You and I can divide on that. As for Espiritu, leave the old woman to me. You can just bet your last dollar, Bisc, that I will work her. You know Kanack, don't you? Rafe is all hunkadoree with the old woman, and it won't be long before I have all of her affairs in my hands."[6]

"But how will that benefit me?" asked Biscailuz.

"Well, you work the European heirs and I will work the old woman—and we'll divy. When you get a case from the European heirs, you take me in and I will manage it. I do believe, Bisc, that if you just keep sober and keep your eyes open for the main chance, you and I can clean up a hundred thousand dollars apiece out of Leonis' estate. I hope to get double that amount out of the old woman before I am done with her. Rafe is now at work. This fellow Stephen M. White is no good for us, and nobody knows that better than I do. Pretty soon, the old woman will drop him like a hot potato. Like so many Indians, when she thinks that a man is not true to her she is willing to drop him and take a new one. That is what she is going to do with Stephen M. White—and I intend to be that new man. All on the square, Bisc. Now, where's that spare dollar?"

At that moment, an old fellow about seven feet tall, with a black patch over one eye and a big cane in his hand, stalked into the office.

Biscailuz said, "Here's your dollar Dick. This is one of the French heirs, Monsieur Jean Leonis. Leave me with him, please."

Their conference ended, Mulligan went to Jake Philippi's.

The tall stranger with the black eyepatch was a brother of Miguel. Being enormously tall, he was correspondingly thin—looking like a portrayal of Don Quixote by the immortal Cervantes. He and Biscailuz were conversing in the Basque language when Mulligan re-entered the sanctu, back from Jake Philippi's.

"Does this caricature speak English?" he inquired.

"Not one word. He has came to see about his interest in the estate, and we were conversing about it when you entered."

"That is all right then, Bisc. I came back to give you some advice. Tangle him up all you can. We must encumber this estate, Bisc. There is no money for us unless we can do it. Now start on on this fellow and tangle him all you can, and then we will go for the others. Remember now, Bisc, no fooling about with this one. For instance, get a deed for his interest, if you can, and then we will fight for it. Oh, and have you a spare dollar, Bisc?"

"Get out," Biscailuz said, giving the leading lawyer a gentle push into the hallway. He then shut the door and returned to Jean Leonis.

As a result of the conference, Jean authorized Biscailuz to represent his claim against the estate of his deceased brother. Biscailuz wrote

245

out an agreement, in the Basque language, and told his visitor, "Go out and show this to your friends, or just read it yourself. If it is satisfactory to you, we will both sign it. If not, we will make it satisfactory. While you are looking it over, I will step into the other room."

In the next room, Biscailuz sat down and hurriedly wrote out a deed and conveyance from Jean Leonis to himself for all the man's right, title and interest in the estate of his deceased brother. He then stepped back into the room where he had left the old Basque—who handed back the paper, saying it looked perfectly satisfactory.

"Then," said Biscailuz, "you sign it and I will sign it."

The lawyer took the paper, stepped into the other room and exchanged it for the deed he had just written. Coming back with it in his hand, he pretended to be still reading it over and then called a notary public from the adjoining office. The old man signed the deed and the notary took his acknowledgment of it. Then Biscailuz signed the agreement. The old man put it in his pocket and went away.

Biscailuz chuckled to himself, "I guess he is pretty well tangled up," and he left to find Richard Mulligan at Philippi's.

Endnotes

1. Horace Bell used the pseudonym "Stephanus Black" here and elsewhere in his manuscript, but the lawyer's real name, Stephen M. White has been substituted.

    Mr. White was one of California's, certainly Southern California's, most famous men. A noted lawyer, a member of the United States Senate, he was largely responsible for the building of Los Angeles' harbor at San Pedro. A bronze statue of him stands in the harbor area. He and Horace Bell jointly represented Espiritu Leonis in her successful suit against the Leonis estate, although Bell could hardly include himself in this story.

Through alcohol White lost both his career and his life; dying while still in his 40's. After White's death in 1901 his estate included "interest in lands in the Leonis estate." It is believed that he and Bell shared a one-half interest in Espiritu's share of the estate.

2. "Sylvanus Mascarbo" is almost certainly a pseudonym. Bell seemed to like to use quasi-latin names such as "Stephanus" and "Sylvanus" in his pseudonyms. Likewise, "Mascarbo" is designed to sound like a Spanish or Mexican name without actually being one! You have seen other examples herein, such as "Saldanyoseguro" and "Muyoscuro," but I have no idea what hidden meaning "Mascarbo" is intended to convey.

3. Miguel did not own the land the Calabasas house stood on, so he could hardly have given it to Espiritu. Hard as he had fought in the courts for the Virgines land grant—in which he contended that Calabasas was part of the Virgines tract—Miguel ultimately lost that case.

4. Jose Mascarel served as mayor of Los Angeles in 1865.

5. This is said to have been Los Angeles' first palimony case. The court ruled that Miguel and Espiritu had had a commonlaw marriage, by virtue of their having lived together some 30 years.

6. Among the other claimants against the estate was 14-year-old Natalia Pryor, Miguel's daughter by Librada Arustica Pryor (who was Mascarel's stepdaughter from the first marriage of his wife Jesus Felis). The pretty young Natalia's claim to her father's estate was ultimately denied—on the basis that Leonis had never formally acknowledged her. Miguel's other daughter (by Espiritu) named Marcelina had died of smallpox nine years prior to Miguel's death.

7. In Bell's original manuscript for this story, twice he wrote the name Plummer and then changed his mind and crossed it out to El Kanacka. It would appear that the Kanacka was a nickname for a man named Rafael Plummer. (Note: I believe that "El Kanacka" means "The Hawaiian." —Ray Phillips) The Plummers and Leonis Family were acquainted. In Juan Menendez' diary (translated) appears "The 13th of March, 1897 Rafael Plummer was here. The 22nd he was here too."

28

Father Jean and Marie Learn of Miguel's Death

Back to the ancient monastery at Cambo. Father Jean was reclining in his easy chair at a window in his private lounging room. Through the grated window, the autumn sun filled the room with warmth and sunshine. Father Jean had just finished reading a letter, which he laid aside while he regaled himself with a glass of his best wine. Presently the errand boy entered, to announce the arrival of Marie Etcheverrigaray and her desire to see Father Jean without delay. She was immediately admitted. As blooming, buoyant and beautiful as ever, the lovely Marie bounced into the room, flourishing a letter in her hand.

"Miguel is coming!" she exclaimed. "He will be on board the next steamer across the Atlantic. Just think. Within a month our flag of freedom will be floating over the battlements of the Pyrenees!"

In his excitement, Father Jean rose from his seat and rushed across the room. Caught up in their fervor over the news, the two threw themselves into each other's arms and commenced to weep. Neither could speak. It was all sobs and tears, until finally Father Jean recovered his self-possession, offered Marie a seat and some wine, and poured another glassful for himself.

"So, you received a letter from Miguel," he said. "I also received a letter—and what is more, I received a draft on the Bank of France for one million francs—the million dollars promised by your fiancee is complete. Everything is in readiness, as you and I both know, and on the very day of

Miguel's arrival at this monastery the revolution will be proclaimed. Our flag can be floated to the breeze—which, by the way, Mademoiselle, you once promised me a flag! Do you recall we discussed the character of the banner we would exhibit to the world? The time has come to show it. Can you have it made soon—the day is now so near."

Marie laughed. "But I have it with me!" she said. From within the folds of her dress she produced and spread upon the table a large embroidered flag. It was a banner of blue silk, with a background range of mountain peaks extending from one edge to the other. The sun rose from behind the tallest peak, and at the mountain base was a great golden lion, resting under a grove of trees with a brood of vigorous cubs. In the foreground was a rich pasture, with domestic animals tended by shepherds and dogs.

"Here is the flag of our new Pyrenean Republic," said Marie. "What do you think of it?"

They fastened the huge banner on the wall. It was a rich affair, embroidered in green, gold and silver. Father Jean thought it was magnificent, brilliant, beautiful—and said so.

"Did you make this?!," he asked incredulously.

"It is all my own work!"

"Your own!" said the father superior. "How long it must have taken you to complete it!"

"Ever since Miguel first went away. Now at last it is finished! It has taken so many years—but that is not too long to work on a banner that heralds the freedom of a new people. We are new—even though descended from one of the most ancient peoples on the earth. Our race is regenerated, Father!"

The father superior pronounced his great satisfaction with the design of the flag and the beauty of its execution. Carefully taking it down and rolling it, he deposited the banner in a safe place.

"When Miguel arrives, we will show it to him," he said, "and then on the very same day it shall be flung to the breeze, our flag of the Pyrenean Republic! Twenty-five thousand of our best men are now armed with repeating rifles and revolvers. Bayonne will be ours and ships will come soon, laden with the munitions of war. Our fight will be furious but not long continued, for these mountains are impregnable. With our population united and armed, Spain to the south, France and the rest of Europe to the north, and Rome and Italy thrown in, which of them could gain and then maintain a foothold in these mountain fastnesses?"

The two co-conspirators then enjoined each other not to say a word of this—even to their most steadfast adherents—not until the day that Miguel Leonis should arrive.

It was only one week later that Marie was called to the monastery. When she entered Father Jean's parlor, she found him in a state of utmost agitation and despondency. Weakly motioning her to a seat, he fell back into his chair in a state of apparent exhaustion. He could not—or would not—speak.

The alarmed Marie refused to leave Father Jean's side, as she tried to attend to him. All her efforts seemed to no avail, however—and yet still she stayed, calling upon an old monk to relieve her at her vigil when it came time for her to sleep. The following morning she was again in the parlor when she noticed a letter that must have fallen to the floor the previous day, near where Father Jean had sat on his easy chair. The inscription on the envelope indicated it had been mailed from Los Angeles, California, on September 21, 1889.

With trembling hands, Marie opened the letter and glanced down at the signature, "Josef Mascarel." Slowly, she read the body of the letter—and then began to weep, "Yesterday, Don Miguel Leonis, of Los Angeles County in California, while on his way from Los Angeles to his rancho El Escorpion, was stricken down by an assassin, who waylaid him in the Cahuenga Pass."

Leonis

29

Mascarel and Jack Haley Stop at El Escorpion
The Tale of the Devil and Tom Walker
A Wedding Celebration

he honest yet wealthy Jose Mascarel of the old Tendajon de La Campana and his companion, the lawyer Haley, were on their way from Santa Barbara to Los Angeles in a private conveyance. That is to say, they rode in an elegant buggy with two spanking horses—with Haley at the helm, whip in hand, and Mascarel at his side.

"I am sorry to hear of Biscailuz' bad luck," Haley said.

"What bad luck?"

"Oh, well, Biscailuz got played out. The hundred thousand dollars or more that he got out of Oxarart's estate was dissipated. How it went, no one can surmise, but he came down to drunkenness and poverty. He was arrested on a charge of forgery and, to save him from punishment, some friends intervened and had him sent to an insane asylum."[1]

"There was no luck about it," observed Mascarel. "It was the absinthe. That French abomination has done more to cause the demoralization of the French people than all else. It may do for soldiers to drink absinthe, because it maddens them and they will rush pell-mell into any danger so long as the influence remains. But when ordinary citizens, especially lawyers, drink absinthe, they are sure to commit suicide or some other crime of the same magnitude—or else go crazy."

"I guess Richard Mulligan will go the same way," said Haley.

"Oh, no. He only drinks whiskey. He is drunk every afternoon and sober the next morning. Doesn't seem to hurt him a bit. He got a good deal of money out of the Leonis estate, didn't he?"

"No," Mascarel answered himself, "Now that I think upon it, I guess not. After Stephen M. White got the old woman's fortune safe into her hands, Mulligan and Biscailuz got the French heirs all tangled up—so that only lawyers collected from Leonis' estate. How was it, Haley, that you didn't get into that?"

"Oh, well, I am old enough and rich enough to keep out of such entanglements, I guess. God help me if I ever get into a scrape such as that was. Several lawyers went crazy.[2] The judge died on the bench while still trying to unravel some of the Leonis matters. They say all of those entanglements were brought about by Mulligan and Biscailuz. I know that Biscailuz never got a dollar out of it. Mulligan picked up a fee here and there—first from one side and then from the other—but I don't think he got anything substantial out of the estate."

"Poor Leonis," said Mascarel. "A more noble, generous, honest and heroic man never stood upon the soil of California. Did you know, Haley, that he sent a million dollars' worth of francs to France?"

"He did?"

"Yes, he did. And had he got back to the Pyrenees he would have become the leader of the Basques' revolution. When he died the proposed revolution died with him, and what became of the money I have no idea. Do you remember the ex-friar Goytino? The one who was in the county jail on a charge of forgery? Well, he is off to Europe now, and I do believe he is trying to hunt down that million dollars. He is not likely to get it—although if rascality will accomplish it, I guess Jean Pierre may succeed. I have written to my brother in Marseilles to inquire as to what became of Leonis' money, but he can throw no light upon the subject. It is not deposited in the Bank of France, and other banks have been investigated without success."

"This Leonis estate business reminds me of the legend of the Devil and Tom Walker. Have you ever heard of it, Senor Mascarel?"

"Not that I know of. Is it an American story?"

"Oh yes, it is all American."

"Tell it to me then, so I can see if it resembles any of the entanglements that dissipated Leonis' estate."

"All right. Did you ever hear tell of Captain Kidd, the great pirate who was hanged in New York?"

"I think so," said Mascarel. "When I was on the Savannah frigate, I once heard some of the sailors talking of Captain Kidd and his buried treasure, which was someplace in the vicinity of New York. Is that the one?"

"Yes, that's it. Now in this legend about Tom Walker, he dug up Captain Kidd's treasure—and this is how he came to get it:

THE DEVIL AND TOM WALKER

Tom Walker was a worthless sort of fellow who lived on Long Island. He was a sort of hunter for small game, a fisherman, and a small-fry wrecker—his greatest wrecking spoil being a plank or a stranded skiff on the shores of Long Island. A very poor fellow was this Tom Walker. One day, while lounging in one of the swamps of Long Island, he sat down on a fallen tree to rest and ruminate over his unsatisfactory condition in life.

He made the remark, 'I wish I were rich. Oh, what lot of good I could do if only I were rich.'

'I can make you rich,' answered a voice. Walker raised his eyes and there before him stood a tall dark-complexioned, black-haired, individual.

'Yes,' the stranger told him. 'I can place in your hands all the gold that you would ever want—and more, too—if you will make a compact with me. Captain Kidd's treasure is buried near here. I will tell you where to find it. if you will satisfy my conditions.'

'State them,' said Tom Walker.

'The first condition is that when you get this gold, you will go over to Wall Street, open a bank, and lend money at five percent per month interest and no less. That is the first condition, Mr. Walker.'

'I accept,' said Tom Walker. 'I would charge them ten percent, if you say so!'

'Oh, no,' answered the man, 'five percent per month is enough. Every man who borrows money at five percent is sure to go to hell, so I am sure to get him. There is no use asking more than that, because we would only catch a smaller number of customers.'

'A bargain so far.' said Tom Walker.

'The second condition, Mr. Walker, is that you will never give a dollar in charity.'

'Oh, I accept to that! What's the next, and how many more are there?'

'One more.'

'Name it.'

'That you will never aid a church or any public charitable institution.'

'All right! I accept that,' said Tom Walker. 'What's next?'

'That is all. But, if you break any of these covenants, you forfeit both your soul and your body—and immediately I take possession.'

'Who are you?' inquired Tom Walker.

'Oh, I have various names. Some call me "Old Nick." Some call me "Lucifer." Others, "The Old Scratch."'

'I guess I will call you the Devil. You must be the Devil himself.'

'That is what I be: the Devil, at your service, sir. And now, if you will come along with me, I will show you the exact spot where all of Captain Kidd's gold is buried—and you can dig it up at your leisure.'

And so the Devil led Tom Walker to a secluded place in the swamp and showed him where to dig. The next day, Tom Walker returned to the spot with digging implements and before long he unearthed bags and bags, filled with golden coins, that he safely transported to Wall Street—where he set up his bank.

Time passed rapidly. Tom Walker got rid of his old wife and married a Fifth Avenue belle, and he set up living in grand style. He had two blooming, beautiful daughters. His entertainments were the grandest, his mansion the finest, his servants the most gorgeously attired, his carriages the best, and his horses of the most exalted breeds. He never lent a dollar for less than five percent per month. He never gave anything in charity, never subscribed to any beneficence, and he turned his back on all the churches and church people. He was a king on Wall Street.

Soon his eldest daughter was engaged to marry a rich banker of London, and the preparations for the ceremony were very elaborate.

The wedding ceremony was preceded by great dinners, balls, drives, yachtings upon the harbor, and every manner of entertainment that could be had for money.

On the day before the wedding, a great dinner was in progress in the large dining hall of the Walker mansion, with Tom Walker seated at the head of the table. Suddenly, and unannounced, a man entered the banquet hall and addressed the assembly thus, 'Mr. Walker, may I speak to all of your most honorable guests? I am a minister of the gospel, and a mortgage is about to foreclosed on my church. Knowing of your great wealth and extreme generosity, Mr. Walker, I have boldly entered your dining room to ask for subscriptions to save my church from the wreck that threatens it. Here is a book, Mr. Walker. Please, put your name down and give me your check.'

Before all the wedding guests, the minister held his book in front of the master of the mansion—who put his name down for five thousand dollars and wrote out his check for that amount to the astonished preacher.

Suddenly there came three great knocks that sounded like the falling of a sledge hammer. The startled company turned toward the upper end of the hall, where a tall dark man stood at a side board.

'Come along, Mr. Walker, you have broken our covenant and I am here to demand possession of your body and your soul.'

The intruder stalked down to the head of the table, where he seized Tom Walker by the nape of his neck. The entire house suddenly opened, and great fumes of sulphurous smoke enveloped the guests. The devil by this time had put on his wings, and he sailed off into infinite space with Tom Walker.

'This is nothing like the estate of Leonis!' exclaimed Mascarel. Leonis got all of his estate by hard work and well-directed enterprise.'

'The devil had nothing from Leonis, it is true,' acknowledged Haley, 'but what is more important, Don Josef, is what became of the estate. In Leonis' case, the lawyers got hold of it, and I tell you the Devil would be merciful compared with lawyers. But let me go on with my story:

'Immediately, the Walker mansion disappeared—and nothing was left to mark the place where it had stood except cinders and ashes. All of the guests disappeared along with the mansion, but still an administrator was appointed to look after the estate of the deceased banquet host. When the administrator went to the vaults on Wall Street, there was nothing to be found but cinders. In the stables, the magnificent horses were there but they were only bones fastened to the mangers—skin and flesh had disappeared and their bones were as white and smooth as though they had been scraped with broken glass. And this, Don Josef, is the end of the episode between the Devil and Tom Walker. The moral of my story is that the Leonis estate—except that which Espiritu got away with—has disappeared much the same way. Nothing is left but cinders and ashes and bare bones."

"Here we are at Calabasas," said Mascarel, as they passed over the mountain crest and stopped to look down. A beautiful valley lay in front of Espiritu's manorial residence, which was nestled among great evergreens. It was now quite late in the afternoon.

"Would you like to stop here and impose on Espiritu's hospitality for the night?" Haley asked.

"Not much," said Mascarel. "The old woman doesn't like me a bit, and I tell you, when Indians get down on a fellow, it can be dangerous. I have not much hair on my head, but I wouldn't risk what is left to be with Espiritu or any of her kin."

As they approached the house, they found everything in fiesta state. The place was ablaze with banners and booths, and music filled the air. The Casa Leonis was decorated from its highest rooftop to its lowest corridor, and the guests numbered in the hundreds. Under the various trees and in the grape arbors leading to the house were tables covered with cold meats, fruits and drinkables.

Colonel Andres Larios y Pacheco stood at the gate that lead from the highway to the front of the house, and Mascarel, being well acquainted with the colonel, addressed him, "Why, Colonel Pacheco, what does all of this mean? I have never seen such a fiesta. Surely, it is a fiesta."

By that time darkness had fallen and hundreds of Chinese lanterns were ablaze. Music and dancing had started in the main hall of the building, and all was uproarious revelry.

"Why, what is the matter? What is this all about?" inquired Mascarel and Haley in one breath. "If there were a church here, I might think it a celebration of some saint's day," Mascarel said. "But Espiritu is not given much to church matters, and the guests I see here are more sinners than saints."

"Did you say Espiritu?" demanded Colonel Pacheco. "You must not speak that way of the illustrious lady who presides over all these people and this palace!"

"Then what shall I call her? How am I to designate her ladyship?" Mascarel responded.

"You must address her—and I will see that you not do otherwise—you must speak of my generous patroness as Dona Maria Espiritu Chijulla de Leonis. She, sir, is the widow and inheritor of the fortunes of El Basco Grande, Don Miguel Leonis, who met with such an unfortunate accident at the Cahuenga four years past. God rest his soul! A good friend of mine was Don Miguel, and he was only an enemy to the bad ones. Always a friend to the poor. May he forever rest in peace."

"But what is this fiesta about?" asked Haley.

"Well, to be brief, this fiesta has been going on for a week now, and will continue for another week. It is all preliminary to the marriage ceremony to be performed."

"What marriage ceremony?" asked Mascarel. "Is Espiritu going to get married?"

"You must not speak of her in such disrespectful tones. Don't do that, Don Jose. It hurts my feelings and offends my sense of honor. I don't want to be driven to resentment, but let me finish this matter, sir, if you please, Dona Maria Espiritu Chijulla de Leonis, the rich widow, is to become the bride of Richard Mulligan, Esq., the great lawyer."

"Oh, rats!" exclaimed Mascarel. "Drive on, Haley!"

Haley cracked the whip and they drove off. "Let's go to the cantina and get a drink before we drive into Los Angeles," he said.

As they drew up to the front of the cantina, an Indian stood by to hold the horses. The two travelers entered and stepped up to the bar.

"Haley, I will take whiskey in mine." It was Richard Mulligan. As he gazed at the ceiling, Mascarel and Haley took note of his apparel—he was wearing a derby hat and a cut-away coat, and in his hand he had a big mahogany cane.

Mascarel paid for the drinks, and he and his companion turned to go back to their carriage.

"Oh, Haley," they heard a voice call from inside, "Have you a spare dollar on you?"

Finis

Endnotes

1. Biscailuz came to a sad end, virtually as described.

2. Lawyer Brunson later became a superior court judge of Los Angeles County. After several years he became the attorney for the Atchison, Topeka & Sante Fe Railway. After several years he left and went to San Bernardino, California to follow his profession, but in a short time thereafter, died.

   Graves wrote about him as follows, "Like many other men of genius, Brunson lacked a balance wheel. He destroyed the vital forces of his physical system, deadened all moral instincts of his nature by indulging in the worst sort of dissipation. He let power and influence and standing and character slip from his grasp, and he died long before his time, as much from the disappointment, which he keenly felt, as from any physical ailment. (All of note 2 is from Graves: *My Seventy Years in California*.)

   Alcohol took a terrible toll among early Los Angeles lawyers.

Leonis

30

Epilogue—Later History of the Family The El Escorpion Ranch and the Leonis Adobe in Calabasas

by Ray Phillips

Espiritu did not marry John Mulligan. As far as is known, there was no other man in her life. However, in the *Los Angeles Times* of November 25, 1895 was an article leaked by Horace Bell saying that, at age 65, Espiritu "had taken to herself a new spouse", 18 year-old Pancho Leiva. We cannot confirm that. Family history only recalls that a Pancho Leiva was living in the Calabasas area up into the 1920's. At one time we had a picture of him, that we may yet run across.

Espiritu did have a son, Juan Menendez, as the story describes. She also had a daughter, Marcelina, by Miguel Leonis. Marcelina died, tragically, in one of Los Angeles' two dreadful smallpox epidemics, when she was just 20. Her death was recorded as happening at El Escorpion. She is not mentioned in Bell's story. The Leonis family moved to Calabasas shortly thereafter, probably in 1880. This almost surely was the result of a corrected survey of El Escorpion that placed the ranch buildings, including Leonis' home, outside the western boundary of the ranch; causing Leonis to lose title to them. Leonis sold El Escorpion in 1885.

Family tradition has it that Leonis found young Juan Menedez sleeping on the hill just across the freeway from the Adobe when he was supposed to be tending a flock of sheep. Leonis lassoed him by one foot, dragged him down to the bottom of the hill, and told him not to come

Leonis Adobe Archives.

Marcelina Leonis
(taken c. 1879)

Espiritu Leonis in 1905. She is sitting in her lawyer's office chair; photographed on the occasion of her victory in the fifteen year fight for her rights.

home. Menendez then apprenticed himself to a blacksmith. He moved back into the Adobe with his mother the day of Leonis' funeral. That is the story. One event throws some doubt on it. Menendez was one of several passengers on the wagon at the time Leonis was killed. He so testified at the inquest.

Juan continued to live at the Adobe with his mother. He married Juana Valenzuela, of San Bernardino, but they had no children. Mrs. Orsua describes how that sad state was rectified. A sister of Juana's, who definitely did not have that problem, found her crying and asked what was the matter. Juana replied, sobbing, "Oh, you have such a wonderful family and I don't have any!" The sister replied, (in effect), "That's all right, Sis, the next one's yours!" And so it happened. When the sister's next baby, a little girl named Maria, was six months old she was given to the Menendez's and raised as their daughter. She did not know until she was nine that her mother was really her aunt!

Many years later, in the 1960's and after they had left the Adobe, through descent from her real parents Mrs. Orsua was able to prove at least part Indian blood, and was granted land on the Morongo Indian Reservation near Cabazon, in the desert on the way to Palm Springs.

As a little girl, Maria's bed was in the small room at the top of the stairs now used as a bathroom. At around nine she was sent to a convent school in Beaumont and came home only on vacations until Espiritu died in 1906. Maria was twelve. Three other girls lived in that room. Two died in childhood. The other lived to be an adult but "went bad" and lost contact with the family. There also was a boy, Librado Verdugo, called "Chief". He was a wild, unhappy youth who tortured animals and at one time almost shot Maria. On one occasion he got into a fight with another boy in the kitchen and they pulled over the big red cabinet and broke everything in it! He lived a dissolute life which ended when he, fairly young but grossly overweight, died while working on a chicken ranch near Lancaster. He had one of a pair of Leonis' nickel plated, ivory handled, .44 caliber Hopkins & Allen revolvers, which he gave to a Lancaster resident who still has it. A picture of it is on display in the Plummer House, on the Leonis Adobe grounds.

*The Leonis Adobe, Calabasas, as it appeared in 1905. Mrs.
Leonis stands just behind the picket fence. her son Juan Menendez stands
among the recently pruned grapevines, with Nellie, the mare. The picket
fence was put up around the front porch to provide a secure play-place for
the children that the Menendezes raised. It was removed when it was no
longer needed. Notice the hitching rail in front of the picket fence, which
was at the edge of what is now Calabasas Road.*

The well, near the house to the east, gave only brackish, bad-
tasting water. Not that a whole lot of water was consumed in those days!
The front of the Adobe was planted in winegrapes and on the first floor
of the tank house both wine and brandy were made. Anyway, soon after
the 1905 photograph of the house, that shows the windmill in place, was
taken the well was abandoned, and another well drilled down near
Calabasas Creek. Still, drinking water was purchased from an itinerant

Espiritu Leonis in the Barnyard at the Leonis Adobe, c. 1902.

tank wagon driver, who served the area. When the Los Angeles Metropolitan Water District was formed, and brought water in from the Owens Valley in 1913, it would supply it only to Los Angeles residents. So

Menendez got the ranch annexed to Los Angeles. Now the Los Angeles city limit to the south is the center of the pepper trees in the Adobe parking and, to the west, about fifty feet beyond the rise at the west end of the Adobe property, where the Adobe property extended before a chunk was sold off by Archie Hansen, Jr. in the early 1950's.

Later, the site of the well and tank house were covered with dirt and asphalt paving. The sites were discovered through the use of the 1905 photograph and the structures re-erected as part of the Adobe's restoration in the early 1960's. The chicken coops and dovecote were replicated after a water color painted in 1913, now in the collection of the Southwest Museum. The wash-shed , bake-oven and bath buildings were replicated from descriptions given by Mrs. Orsua.

In 1910 Maria Johnson, her name, as she was never formally adopted by the Menendezes, married Pedro Orsua, a young Mexican from Sonora. The Menendezes opposed the marriage, as both partners were severely under-age. Indeed, they had to lie in order to get a marriage license! However, the marriage lasted, eventually producing eighteen children, of which sixteen lived to adulthood.

The Orsua family lived at the Leonis Adobe only part of the time, although their first three children were born there. More about the Orsuas later.

Leonis' ranch in Calabasas contained, presumably, some 8000 acres, although title to much of it was contested. The original barn, blacksmith shop and corrals stood across Calabasas Road from the Adobe. In 1907 they all burned; presumably torched by enemies of the family. When, in the 1980's the small buildings that had stood there since the 1920's and 1930's were razed, archaeologists were hired to search for the barn. They found nothing. Pedro Orsua told me that he had used the charred but salvageable boards that survived the fire to build a small shack on the site next to the road. There, he sold soft drinks to travelers, as the road was the main route between Los Angeles and Ventura and points north. The bottles were cooled by being placed in a box with a wet gunnysack thrown over it.

Leonis Adobe Archives.

The Leonis Adobe, c. 1923. At the rear of the house, the Agoure's addition is under construction. Above the roof can be seen the chimney to the living room fireplace, added by the Agoure family. Behind the oak tree an old frame building is still standing. This had been used by the Menendez family, half for food storage, the other half as living quarters for an elderly relative. When he died he was buried in the family cemetery, across Calabasas Road. At the far right the debris, and the barrels, would seem to indicate that the outbuilding where wine was stored had just been torn down.

In 1912 Pedro Orsua helped Juan Menendez build the present barn. It was not where it is now, having originally stood quite far to the northeast, where the Ventura Freeway now runs. It was moved once before the freeway was built in the early 1950's to a location some 50 feet east of where it now stands. In the mid-1960's CALTRANS bought additional land across the back of the Adobe property for a future off-ramp.

Now, in 1991, construction is scheduled to start in the next year or two. The barn was moved to its present (third!) location after the mid-1960's purchase in order to preserve it, as its rear half was on CALTRANS property.

In 1921 title passed out of the family. It would seem that Juan Menendez, perhaps partially disabled by poor vision, had lived almost entirely by selling off portions of the ranch. He finally ran out of ranch and money. He finally lost the ranch, including the Adobe, now down to something over five acres, to Martin Agoure. Agoure owned a large ranch just to the west, where the city of Agoura Hills now stands. Agoura is a corruption of Agoure, misspelled in an old deed. We are not sure whether the transaction was a sale or foreclosure, but Agoure moved a small house onto a lot he owned in Canoga Park, and Mr. and Mrs. Menendez moved there. Juan Menendez died about 1924, we do not know the date of Mrs. Menendez' death, or even the address of the house.

Martin Agoure's wife made sure the family moved to the Adobe, although they also had a house in Los Angeles. Over the next several years the Agoures substantially modernized the house. Oak hardwood was laid over the Adobe's pine floors. Electricity and plumbing were added. A two-story extension was added to the rear to provide bedrooms and bathrooms. In the living room a partition wall was removed, as were the corner cupboards (which have been restored to their original positions), and a large volcanic-stonefaced fireplace was added in the northeast corner.

A door was cut through the adobe wall to provide direct access to the dining room. The dining room and kitchen had raised wooden floors laid above the original adobe, the walls were plastered and painted, the brick fireplace refaced with volcanic stone and the kitchen modernized. Outside, to the northwest, a large cage was built for the family monkey. A son, Lester, still living and enjoying retirement, says that the environment was perfect for a boy to grow up in!

Unfortunately, in 1931 the Agoures lost the place through foreclosure. After that the house had a series of owners, being occupied some-

Ruins of Leonis' lime kiln on the South bank of Bell Creek. The only remaining evidence of early habitation remaining on El Escorpion.

times by owners, other times by tenants. In the early 1930's the house was used for a time as a chicken-dinner restaurant. It has been said that at another time the house was used for a retirement home and an additional stairway added to the front porch. This has not been verified, and there is no sign that a second stair had ever been attached to the front.

When this writer visited the house in the early spring of 1947 he went out early on a Sunday morning, early so that the low rays of the sun would allow light to reach under the deep porches and illuminate the walls of the building and make a good picture. While I was setting up my camera the husband of the family came out to see what I was doing in his front yard. He promptly invited me in to breakfast with his family, which included his wife, a young son, and his mother. After a delicious breakfast of pancakes and bacon I was sent on my way with an armload of Lilac blossoms. It has been 44 years, but it seems only yesterday. A print from a photograph taken that day is on display at the Adobe, in the Plummer House.

Either the same day, or within a few days, I took several photographs of El Escorpion, which Leonis had sold in 1885. It had been used for various purposes, including a dairy, but in 1947 the ruins of at least two adobes survived, and Leonis' large two-story barn was complete and in good condition. The general area was subdivided soon after 1949 and

Photograph by Chet Cohen, Leonis Adobe Archives.

Ruins of one of the Adobe ranch houses at El Escorpion in 1947.
Very soon after the area was subdivided, the ruins of at least two houses
were demolished. The large barn lasted until sometime in the 1960's,
when it, too, was razed.

all traces of habitation removed with the exception of the barn. It survived until the 1960's when it, too, was torn down. By the late 1980's the
entire area where the houses and barn had stood had been filled many
feet deep, leveled and houses built on it. Nothing survives, not even the
terrain, nothing, that is, except a few brick down at the foot of the steep
bank bordering Bell Creek, where a few worn brick mark the site of
Leonis' lime kiln.

Leonis' barn, taken in 1947. Two story adobe barn built in the 1870's as part of the El Escorpion ranch buildings. Destroyed in the 1960's when the area was subdivided.

The Leonis Adobe, in Calabasas, was more fortunate. In 1950 Archie Hansen and his son, Archie Hansen, Jr. bought a ranch in Calabasas and developed it into what is now the city of Hidden Hills. Archie Hansen, Jr. bought the Leonis Adobe and moved in with his wife and family. Mr. Hansen made a number of minor changes in the Adobe, while leaving the historic structure intact. Most of his work was careful restoration. He repaired and restored the upstairs porch railing, including the fretwork portion, for example. On the rear, he remodeled the Agoure's addition, which was removed entirely in the mid-1960's as part of that restoration. Fortunately neither the Agoures or the Hansens removed any substantial part of the house as it stood about 1880, they simply covered it with new material that we were able to remove later. Unfortunately,

Mr. Hansen did demolish all of the outbuildings with the exception of the barn, but by 1950 they were only dilapidated wrecks.

In 1954 the Hansens left the house, and not long after rented it to the well-known character actor, John Carradine, who lived there with several of his sons for about five years. He was the last actual tenant. According to Mr. Hansen, Carradine paid rent occasionally for a while. Then Mr. Hansen simply gave up trying to collect! The boys had a wonderful time. They had trees to climb and horses to ride. John Carradine built the mangers in the barn, according to one son.

By the early 1960s the Adobe was owned by a Beverly Hills real estate developer who wanted to build a supermarket on the premises, which would have spelled the doom of the Adobe which, by now was occupied only by a caretaker. The local citizens, spirited largely by Laura Gaye, attempted to get the State to buy the property for a roadside rest, the County or the City to buy it for a park. Nothing worked.

Finally came the dreaded application for a demolition permit. As the story was told to me, the clerk was primed and ready. When the application was presented at the counter the clerk asked, "Where is the signature?" Nonplussed, the messenger took back the application and left to secure the signature and return the next morning. According to the story, bulldozers were waiting on the property, just waiting for the permit. What did happen, for sure, was that before the messenger returned the recently formed Cultural Heritage Board of Los Angeles held its first meeting and promptly declared the Leonis Adobe "Los Angeles Historic-cultural Monument Number One." This triggered a six month hold on demolition and saved the Adobe, at least temporarily. By the way, the clerk was careful not to say that the demolition application required a signature, as it did not. The application was valid without one, and could have been filed if the messenger had only asked the crucial question, "Does it need one?"

During this period a lovely public-spirited lady, Mrs. Walter (Kay) Beachy, who had lived nearby since coming out from Chicago around 1939, aided by the demolition hold, bought the property from the developer. Her plan was to preserve the Adobe and the land immediately around it, and develop the balance as a low-density center for handcrafts and a nursery.

While negotions took place, the last caretaker had left, and the local children began to vandalize the place. They broke every window, tore the shutters off the walls, broke up the fretwork balcony railing with hammers and baseball bats, tore off the banister railing and stuffed it down a chimney, set fires that fortunately went out, and much more .

Mrs. Beachy put up a fence and we members of the newly-formed Leonis Adobe Assn. boarded up the window and doors each Saturday. Each Sunday the kids would rip off the boards and continue. Finally Mrs. Beachy moved a house trailer and a family over next to the building and vandalism stopped . In a few weeks children, hardly any over twelve, had done more damage than had been done in the previous 120 years.

By this time the writer had been elected president of the Association. Two splendid architects were on the Board, Ralph Bowerman, now deceased, and Ray Girvigian, who later worked on the restoration of the Capitol building in Sacramento. Mrs. Beachy gave the Association, $40,000 from her charitable trust. With it the Association "bought" from her $33,000 worth of land, at her cost, immediately surrounding the buildings. With the balance, and money that it could raise, the Association started restoration. The two architects planned, the writer hired, supervised and, frequently, fired. In those long-ago days old houses were torn down, not restored, and it was very difficult to find workmen sensitive to restoration, and impossible to find any who had actually done any. The Association Board worked hard raising money. We would work until money ran out, raise some more and work until it was gone!

About this time we discovered, probably through Mrs. Beachy, that Mr. and Mrs. Pedro Orsua were still alive, well, and living in Milpitas, near San Jose. My wife Nancy and I drove up to visit them. We taped their recollections of the Adobe and were preparing to leave when one of them asked, "Aren't you going to need caretakers?" "Yes". "Can we come down and be your caretakers?" Well, we were overjoyed, and as soon as the house was made marginally habitable they came down to the house to which Mrs. Orsua had been brought as a baby in 1896, and where they had not lived in over forty years. They were our caretakers for the next several years More than that, they gave us many family mementos, told us where to place furniture, identified photographs, and were delightful friends, as several of their children continue to be.

Finally Mr. Orsua developed lung cancer, and one lung was removed. While he was completely cured, he did not feel able to continue at the Adobe. Each of them lived to a ripe old age, and we remember them with gratitude. The string of red peppers hanging next to the kitchen window (1991) were grown in their garden at the Morongo Indian Reservation, and given to us on the occasion of a visit there.

Mr. Orsua died in 1978, and his wife a year later. Both are buried in the San Jose Mission cemetery.

As soon as the Adobe could be made presentable, and furnished with antique furniture and showcases loaned to us by the History Division of the Natural History Museum of Los Angeles County, the Adobe was staffed with volunteers and opened to the public. With private gifts and donations and a Fiesta held yearly for over 15 years the Association Board of Directors, never more than eleven members, restored, furnished and kept open the Adobe for its first twenty years with no government funds whatsoever. The Board is proud of that.

About that time Mrs. Beachy, tragically, had a stroke and died soon after, leaving her Calabasas property to her charitable trust. The trustees, headed by Mrs. Beachy's sister Mrs. Emlyn (Elaine) Williams, voted to give the Calabasas property to the Leonis Adobe Association. Since then the Association has used funds generated by these properties for the Adobe, which has over 10,000 visitors a year, about half of which are school children on field trips. It has moved and restored the Plummer House (California State Historical Monument #160), has aided, and will continue to aid, other private and public historical restoration projects, and is preparing to turn the vacant land east of the Sagebrush Cantina

Restaurant into a park. The Association will soon celebrate thirty years of dedicated commitment to the Leonis Adobe.

Descendants of Nettie Pryor, Leonis' daughter by Mascarel's step-daughter, live in Southern California. Leonis' only child by Espiritu, a daughter named Marcelina, died when she was twenty. Espiritu's only other child, Juan Menendez, was the last of her line. Leonis' nephew, Jean (John) Leonis later founded the city of Vernon. His grandson, Leonis Malburg, is Vernon's long-time mayor and generous friend of the Association.

If CALTRANS on the north and the Los Angeles Road Department on the south will stop looking at the Adobe property with such covetousness, the Leonis Adobe and its Association can look forward to a long and happy future! ❧

— Ray Phillips
President, Leonis Adobe Assn.

BIBLIOGRAPHY

Barrows, H. D.
1900   "Jose Mascarel." Annual Publication, *Historical Society of Southern California ans Pioneer Register,* Los Angeles, 1899.

Bell, Horace
1927   *Remninscences of a Ranger,* Wallace Hebberd, Santa Barbara.

1930   *On the Old West Coast,* Lanier Bartlett (ed.), Grosset & Dunlap, New York.

Bissell, Clifford H.
1960   "The French Language Press in California," *California Historical Society Quarterly,* California Historical Society, San Francisco.

Cohen, Chester G.
1989   "El Escorpion," monograph, Periday Co., Woodland Hills.

Douglass, William and John Bilboa
1975   *Amerikanuak: Basques in the New World,* University of Nevada Press, Reno.

Edberg, Bob
1978   "A Brief History of the Rancho El Escorpion at the Mouth of Bell Canyon and the Moores Homestead at the Mouth of Moores Canyon," research paper, California State University, Northridge.

Gaye, Laura B.
1975   *Land of the West Valley,* Argold Press, Encino.

Graves, J. A.
  1927   *My Seventy Years in California,* The Times-Mirror Press, Los Angeles.
          Leonis' name does not appear in the index, but his name is men-
          tioned several times in the text and a story is told about his experience
          with a lawyer. Portraits of several lawyers appear, as well as other
          prominent Southern Californians.

Gudde, Erwin G.
  1969   *California Place Names,* University of California Press, Berkeley.

Harrison, Benjamin S.
  1953   *Fortune Favors the Brave,* The Ward Ritchie Press, Los Angeles.

Henstell, Bruce
  1980   *Los Angeles: An Illustrated History,* Alfred Knopf, New York.

Layne, J. Gregg
  1935   *Annals of Los Angeles,* California Historical Society, San Francisco.

Loyer, Fernand and Charles Beaudreau (ed.)
  1932   *Le Guide Francais de Los Angeles et du Sud de la Californie,* The Franco
          American Publishing Company, Los Angeles.

Pitt, Leonard
  1970   *The Decline of the Californios,* University of California Press, Berkekley.

Robinson, W. W.
  1966   "The Spanish and Mexican Ranchos of San Fernando Valley," South-
          west Museum Leaflet, Highland Park, Los Angeles.

Russell, J. H.
  1959   *Cattle on the Conejo,* Thomas Litho & Printing Co., Los Angeles.

Sanchez, Nellie Van De Grift
  1922   *Spanish and Indian Place Names of California,* A. M. Robertson, San
          Francisco.

Leonis

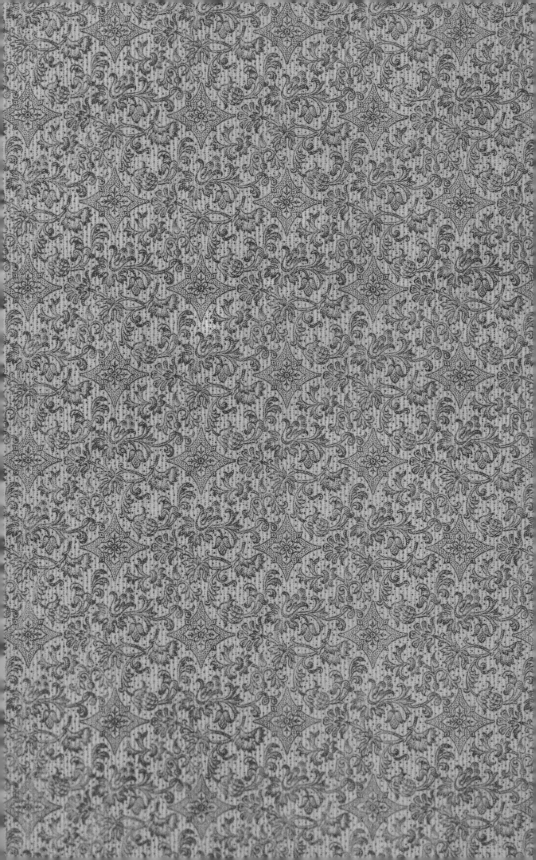